# Jongleur Songs of Old Quebec

MARIUS BARBEAU

# JONGLEUR SONGS
# OF OLD QUEBEC

*Interpreted into English by*
Sir Harold Boulton and Sir Ernest MacMillan

*Decorations by*
Arthur Price

RUTGERS UNIVERSITY PRESS
*New Brunswick*      *New Jersey*

*Published in Canada by*
THE RYERSON PRESS
*Toronto*

Under the patronage of
THE NATIONAL MUSEUM OF CANADA
and the ægis of the
JOHN SIMON GUGGENHEIM MEMORIAL FOUNDATION

Manufactured with the aid of a grant from the Ford Foundation

Designed by Leonard W. Blizard

Manufactured in the United States of America
by Quinn & Boden Company, Inc., Rahway, New Jersey

To the memory

of

SIR HAROLD BOULTON, Bart., C.V.O., C.B.E.

# WHAT WAS A JONGLEUR?

The definition of "Jongleur" is given in the *Standard Dictionary of Folklore, Mythology, and Legend* (Maria Leach, Ed., Funk & Wagnalls, New York, 1950. Vol. II, 557):

> A strolling performer of the Middle Ages whose repertoire included juggling, acrobatics, singing, and playing of instruments for casual entertainment. While the troubadour composed and performed in courtly style, the jongleur was the purveyor of popular song, dance, and tale, and may be credited with much of the transmission of such lore throughout Europe, as well as with the composition of some songs, and the reduction of troubadour works to popular form. The jongleurs' function was taken over to some extent by Gipsies who came into Europe, many as itinerant entertainers, as the wandering minstrel was beginning to disappear.

This definition may be adapted to the French and Canadian repertoire as follows: The French jongleur goes back in time to the beginnings of the folk language in France. Many traditional songs of his composition commemorate events and illustrate customs in the twelfth century and the Middle Ages. Their prosody conforms to the basic patterns of the Romance dialects of Spain, Italy, and France, as transmitted orally, and their themes are quite similar. The majority of the jongleurs' songs antedate the advent of printing, in the fifteenth and sixteenth centuries. The New-World settlers brought the songs to North America as part of their French heritage two or three hundred years ago. They often went on transforming them, adding new features and tunes, thus keeping the "jongleur" spirit alive after it had wilted in the motherland.

# PREFACE

New France, in the first part of the seventeenth century, consisted of three main French colonies in North America—Canada, Acadia, and the Missouri and Mississippi river valleys, including Louisiana. Canada's frontiers reached from the lower Saint Lawrence to the present Ontario and beyond, while Acadia, a crown colony by itself, was situated in what is now Nova Scotia and New Brunswick. Almost to the present day, these two countries have considered themselves independent of each other, with Louisiana the third part of New France in the New World.

The language and folk traditions of ancient France followed the settlers and adventurers into the New World. Time, distance, and misfortune were not enough to blunt the racial patrimony of old; they only served to enhance its value as a solace in the wilderness. Songs, tales, and handicrafts survived the change and centuries, as if conserved under a white blanket of snow.

The forty-two folksongs in this book are barely representative of the whole French repertory in North America, which is highly varied and diversified. They may serve only as samples out of a multitude, for they do not cover the whole field either in space or in time. Nearly all are drawn from the earliest two or three thousand records made by the author for the National Museum of Canada from 1915 to 1925. They were prepared mostly for the use of singers and musicians in festivals and recitals; this is an editorial method midway between the exact reproduction of the raw documents and the final *rédaction critique* adopted by scholars in the study of classical archeology and restoration. Eventually these songs should incorporate all their versions comparatively analyzed, so as to bring out the essentials in their plenitude. But this fastidious approach was not practical at the time, and it cannot be considered here because of space limitations.

vii

Sir Harold Boulton, whose publications on the folksongs of Great Britain are noteworthy, about 1927, happened to come across some Canadian folksongs of our collections and was irresistibly drawn to them. The result, in the few following years, was his apt and spirited adaptations in English of well over one hundred texts. More than twenty of them, with piano harmonizations by Arthur Somerwell, were published in London in 1927, and a much larger set was left in the care of the author for eventual publication. It is from this collection that the present forty-two songs have been selected.

The valuable index of Canadian versions of folksongs at Les Archives de Folklore, Université Laval, Québec, was consulted and utilized here. Grateful thanks!

MARIUS BARBEAU

## ABOUT THE DECORATIONS

The Canadian artist Arthur Price has drawn his models for the medieval jongleurs here illustrated from the following sources:

The frieze of the XIIIth century church of Adderbury, near Banbury, Oxon, England, which embodies in its long lateral band a number of itinerant jongleurs with their instruments and of contemporary allegorical beasts. (Thanks to Lord Elton for the photographs utilized.)

*La musique des Troubadours,* by Jean Beck (Les Musiciens célèbres, Paris, 1928).

*Les Vilains dans les œuvres des Troubadours,* by Alcius Ledieu (Paris, 1890).

*Cours complet d'éducation musicale et de chant choral en quatre livres,* by J. Hanson, A.M., and M. Dautremer, Vols. I and II.

The initials on each drawing refer to the source from which it was taken:

Add—Adderbury church frieze
JB—Jean Beck
AL—Alcius Ledieu
HD—Hanson–Dautremer

# CONTENTS

ix

x

xi

# THE DISCOVERY OF THE FOLKSONGS
# OF FRENCH CANADA

The Indians occupying the "Grand Ripvière de Canada" four hundred years ago were Huron-Iroquois. The name of *Canada* itself, in their language, means "village folk." When first encountered in 1534 by Jacques Cartier, the Breton pilot and sea captain of Saint-Malo in the service of King François I of France, they were on a fishing and war expedition near the mouth of the great waterway now called the Saint Lawrence. They greeted the French seaman with strange dances and songs and allowed him to plant on the Gaspé beach a wooden cross surmounted by the fleur-de-lis: the symbol of an era still to come in the New World. But their permanent village stood a long way up the river at Stadacona, near the spot where Samuel de Champlain later established Quebec. Of all the North American natives they were foremost in the earliest records of discovery.

The study of a handful of their descendants, which fell to my lot early in my career as a young ethnologist for the National Museum of Canada, looked rather unpromising. Only half-breeds, all of them Catholic, were left at their village of Lorette near Quebec; they had forsaken their customs and language; they used only French, like their next-door neighbors, the French-Canadian habitants of Beauport and Charlesbourg. Some of the men still were hunters and trappers in the northern wilderness or guides to sportsmen. Others were homebodies—craftsmen making snowshoes and sleighs, women producing baskets, toys, and moose-hair-embroidered moccasins. Yet it seemed wise for me to begin near home before exploring farther Indian territories where frontier life still persisted or was about to fade out of existence.

My own incentive to proceed to Lorette in the spring of 1911 went back to impressions I had received in my boyhood at school. A Huron priest, the only one of his decadent nation ever ordained, had come as a guest of honor to the parish academy where I was going through the first grades. He had stepped upon the stage and had chanted and danced in the manner of his forebears of the woodlands. His strange tunes and pantomime were those of *La Découverte* or Discovery, *Weneeya,* and the scalp dance *Yanikoya.*

These chants brought to me a new and deep impression, so different were they from our own, so dramatic! They came from another world—that of the Indians in the wilderness I had heard of. The Indian priest himself was a colorful survivor of a storied past, for the Indians in their primitive state have long since vanished from French Canada. His long aquiline nose and profile, his coppery brown skin, his lustrous black eyes, his mellow yet sonorous and chesty voice were hauntingly magnetic. His noble presence, as he wheeled about in a circle as if around a tree, filled the whole space. Here was a war chief on a forest trail, shading his brow with one hand and stooping forward until he spied a white man in the distance, rushed for him, knocked him down with a tomahawk or war club, raised his scalp with a sharp knife, and then whooped for victory.

Entering the field as an ethnologist on the Huron reserve near Quebec, I inquired about the old priest of my school days, whose name was Prosper Vincent, the one who had sung and danced *Weneeya* and *Yanikoya.* He was still alive, though old and feeble by then. I found him most friendly, and lonely. He proved to be by far the best informed among these people on old songs, dances, legends, and ways of life. Nearly seventy songs were recorded with him on the Standard Edison phonograph, also a number of folktales and traditions. Some of these have been published since; others are preserved at the National Museum of Canada. They were saved in the nick of time for posterity, for the old man died soon afterward, the last of his type.

My Huron research extended over the better part of three years and was more fruitful than had been anticipated. It led to other research among the neighboring tribes of the northeastern woodlands, in particular among the allied Iroquoians of the Confederacy of the Five Nations. These tribes once occupied most of what is now Ontario and the western half of the present state of New York. Rather civilized and politically advanced town dwellers, they were Canadians by name, tillers of the soil, playing a predominant role in the colonial history of Canada and the eastern United States. No government would count without them, and often they called the tune.

This study of the Indians unexpectedly opened the door upon another field, that of the French traditions of the region. It awakened interest in the recollections brought over from the motherland by the early settlers who, from 1635 to 1680 (a few even earlier), came to the shores of the Saint Lawrence, to Acadia (now Nova Scotia) on the Atlantic, to the Great Lakes, to the Ohio or Belle Rivière, to the Missouri, and to Louisiana. For, at one time, two-thirds of North America were explored or colonized by the French, who readily made friends with the Indians.

The ancestral traditions of the French, enriched by the settlers and colonists and voyageurs, remained alive and vocal down to our own time. But they were taken for granted and remained obscure. Nobody thought they were worth recording and preserving, still less that in a changed mechanized world they would come to the verge of extinction.

While I was gathering Indian legends with the old half-breed Prudent Sioui (*Tsiwe'*, which means Lousy), a former hunter with dark eyes and a sullen countenance, and his pale-faced wife Marie Picard, I was hesitant when they offered me some tales of mixed origin—part Huron and part French—like the "Tree of Dreams" (a Christmas story about an apparition of the Blessed Virgin in a tree at night and a veteran hunter who would adore the Divine Child in her arms) or like the tradition of Carcajou, a young Indian of high rank who fell into evil ways and sold his soul, like Dr. Faust, to the great Snake or Dragon for a bottle of rum that never emptied however much was poured from it, a sack of gold ever brimful, and a prolonged life of frivolity and debauch.

My idea at the start had been to concentrate on ethnography, but later it expanded to include old French traditions and lore as well. This was reasonable since frequently the Indian and French lore had become so intermingled that it was not easy to unravel their blended fabric. During a short period of transition, Huron tales, like the Iroquoian cosmogony of Tsesta and Tawiscaron (Fire and Flint), the divine Twins who fashioned the Great Earth Island at the beginning, were followed by *Eau de la fontaine de Paris* and *La Princesse des sept montagnes vertes*. Then it was agreed to incorporate French-Canadian folklore into the regular Museum program. This policy has been continued and even expanded to include English and other white-man's lore, to the present time.

When dark-eyed Sioui and his pale-faced wife brought forth Indian songs and lullabies, like *Nenki nenki nenkok,* to put a child to sleep on a cradleboard, the phonograph entry on an index card was filed away among the Huron-Iroquois materials. But when, soon after, Mrs. Sioui intoned *La Fille du roi d'Espagne,* it sounded quite different, and the entry on a card went into another file, among French tunes. But the French songs were not then acceptable in spite of their charm, modal quality, rhythm, and lilt. They were brushed aside because, it was then believed, they had been collected and published long before (in the 1860s) by Ernest Gagnon, of Quebec, in his *Chansons populaires du Canada,* a well-known book that has run into several editions and contains about 100 songs. It was supposed to have drained the field to the very bottom, so nobody considered it worthwhile to revisit the sources.

I decided to look into this promising avenue and proceeded down the Saint Lawrence. Early in May (1916) I packed up my phonograph and a large supply of blank wax records, plenty of field notebooks with red covers, index cards to fill a whole drawer. For if you wish a thing to happen you must visualize it first, make ready for it, and expect it, and then there is every chance that it will come to pass.

I landed at Éboulements, Charlevoix county, in the foothills between Quebec and Murray Bay on the northeast shore, one evening after the setting sun had painted the wide expanse of the river red: a sign of fair weather for the morrow, and for me a prognostic of a rich harvest in the summer months to come.

The next morning, strolling along the dusty village road close to the seashore at Lower Éboulements (which means Landslide), I noticed an old woman rocking herself on her veranda. She was knitting a pair of woolen stockings. Smiling, she greeted me, as the people in the country always do, stranger or friend. This smile was like an invitation to come and sit beside her while she went on with her work.

What, I asked, did she sing to her children or her grandchildren? Her answer was (my red notebook and fountain pen were already at work), *Mon petit Jésus, bonjour! C'est la poulette grise. . . .*

This easy entry into the realm of folksongs beginning at the cradle and in the nursery did not permit of any hesitation or delay. I spent

xvi

the next few days on the same and neighboring verandas facing the Saint Lawrence, recording many songs, now in shorthand, then on the phonograph as well, and the informants enjoyed hearing their own voices reproduced on the recordings. During the evenings, for a change, I went about calling upon other old people in the village. Every one was interested in this strange but welcome pastime. And nearly everybody had something to offer.

Elizabeth Tremblay, the eighty-year-old grandmother whom I had first consulted, while she smoked her clay pipe, furnished some valuable items so far unknown. They were a surprise to me, as they had the familiar ring of true folksongs, to which I soon grew accustomed.

Among them were *Mon père n'avait fille que moi*—My father had me for an only daughter, Yet he sent me out to sea. The captain in command, . . . etc. (a lively dance song); *La Belle a pris son miroir*—The pretty maid held up her mirror. Her young brother, beholding her, said, "What's the use to be so pretty, . . . etc."; *L'Herbe verdit tous les printemps*—The grass grows green every spring . . . etc. (a shepherd love song).

Very soon I climbed the nearby hills—about 1,500 feet high—to the mountain village of Upper Éboulements, whose row of white houses leads up to the parish church with a high spire. There I found a treasure trove of tales and songs, and much of the following month was spent there. By a strange anomaly, the part of Éboulements richest in folklore was a long slope called Misery Row: *le Rang de la Misère*. Fairy tales there dovetailed with folksongs. The Bouchard and Tremblay families knew the most. Père Mailloux proved to be unsurpassed in his stories of *Talon-rouge* (Red-heel), *Tarabon*, the sorcerer Merlin, and *La Syrène*. Jean Bouchard, who claimed he could do as well, told the tales of Petit Jean in a cycle, like those of Paul Bunyan in the woodlands of the United States.[1] Petit Jean, the puny boy of Canadian folktale, was the last in a family of several children born of poor parents. In spite of wretched beginnings, he managed to win the good will of a fairy and thereafter enjoyed good luck. He also had plenty of pluck, so he quickly rose in the scales, performed herculean tasks, slaughtered monsters and giants, and in the end married the princess whom he had delivered from a dragon.

Folksongs, however, remained the main pursuit of that revealing

---

[1] The theory has even been advanced that Bunyan's wonder stories are the offspring of Petit Jean's.

summer which was replete with discovery. Of a number of good folk singers, two will serve as typical: Mme. Jean Bouchard and Louis l'Aveugle, the Blind. All their songs were traditional, songs which had come down from other folk like themselves and had been learned by ear at an early age, usually in childhood, and were often rehearsed during a lifetime.

Mme. Jean Bouchard, of Upper Éboulements, was the wife of a former lumberjack and laborer. They had lived abroad with their family and only recently had come back home very poor, and the husband had lumbago. Their family of boys and girls was growing lustily about them. Mme. Bouchard was gentle, sweet, and patient, with a saddened smile. Her thin though "long" voice was not without charm; it was tinged with melancholy. Her songs were recorded at the rate of about twenty per sitting. In the long exile of her family, she had stopped chanting her home songs but had not forgotten them. The chief feature of her repertory was its domesticity and simple faith in religious legends, in miracles, in the lives of saints. Medieval *complaintes* or ballads of the come-all-ye kind were by no means lacking, and I eagerly sought them. She also gave me love songs of the *pastourelle* and nightingale-messenger class. She sang: *La bergère muette—Écoutez la complainte,* in which the Blessed Virgin appears to the mute shepherdess and by a miracle makes her speak before she dies and goes to heaven; *Blanche comme la neige* (White as the snow), a ballad of a maiden kidnaped on horseback by three bold knights, but who feigns death to foil their designs; *Derrière chez mon père, vole, mon cœur!,* a spinning and work song with chorus: *J'ai cueilli la belle rose* (I have plucked the pretty rose), a dance song on a theme of gallantry and love.

Louis Simard l'Aveugle, the roving blind minstrel of the North Shore, belonged to another class. Blind since childhood, he had been an entertainer from his youth and was now past sixty. In the summer he traveled about on foot, with his fiddle or table harp (*bioune*). Everywhere in two or three counties, from Charlevoix to Lake Saint John and the Saguenay, he was well known and welcomed by all. And he chose the best house and table whenever he stayed for a few days. There he would give songs, yarns, vaudeville, his only reward being hospitality and cheer. And he spread news and gossip wherever he went. His repute reached far and wide. Soon it came to my ears and I wanted to meet him. The problem was to find him on the remote byways when no one was ever sure of his whereabouts.

Someone assured me that he would arrive at Saint-Irénée, a coast parish to the east, for his annual pilgrimage to his birthplace there on the feast of Saint Anne, July 25. So I packed up my phonograph and plenty of blank records and took passage on a paddle-wheel boat to Saint-Irénée on the eve of Saint Anne's celebration. I landed there at night and, at a boardinghouse, I inquired about Louis l'Aveugle. Good news for me: he had come the day before. So I waited impatiently to see him the next day.

It was a sunny morning as I went out to explore and inquire about him among the scattered houses on the tidal shore. Soon I saw a strange-looking old man with long locks of gray hair and vacant facial expression who seemed to follow his cane as he slowly stepped forward in my direction. Without doubt this was l'Aveugle, the blind singer. I stopped in front of him and he paused to size me up. Who was I? He could not make out, for we had never met before. Blind as he was, his perception was keen, for in no time he "knew" me to his own satisfaction and understood my "business"—looking for songs and yarns. He invited me to walk in at the next house for a cup of coffee. This place was like home for him, and he could bring in a guest. This was Mme. Gautier's house. She greeted us just as if we were expected. And so—I was hunting for folksongs and yarns! I would get them in plenty! I mentioned my phonograph. He knew about such contrivances. He would sing in it and then hear his own voice—what fun! Yes, I agreed, quite satisfied with the way things were going, even before breakfast! Now in advance I wished to hear his famous ballad *Pyrame et Thisbé*, 260 lines long, telling the old tale used by Shakespeare in *A Midsummer Night's Dream*. Its origin was in Asia Minor, long ago. We sipped our coffee over the thought of his giving the whole of that come-all-ye in which two Babylonian lovers were opposed by Thisbé's family. The pair cut a hole through a stone wall to speak secretly of their love to each other and to plan an escape at dawn. They ran away separately into a lion-infested desert, only to meet with a tragedy of error there.

To my utter disappointment and surprise, Louis l'Aveugle stopped short after having intoned: *Deux jeunes cœurs jadis.* . . . But why? Go on, go on! He informed me that this was not the time for him to sing such frivolity. The feast of Saint Anne was about to begin. Saint

xix

Anne was his great patron saint. He had come a long way from Mille Vaches, or Thousand Cows (Sea Cows), on the lower Saint Lawrence, to confess his sins to the parish priest, receive Holy Communion, and to do his annual conscience searching and cleaning. A job!

I thought I could overcome his objection with the offer of paying for his services, so much per day, so much per hour. But nothing would induce him to change his mind. I had to go back empty-handed to my headquarters, yet with a promise. In a week, if I came back, he would do all I wanted, sing, dance, stand on his head! He would sing for the phonograph *Pyrame et Thisbé, Damon et Henriette, Saint Alexis* (the saint under the staircase), and all kinds of *tordions*, God bless you!

A week later I renewed my visit with my equipment and a great craving for songs and yarns. This time there was no disappointment. In less than three days I had exhausted my local supply of wax blanks and had taken down ninety songs. Some of these were recorded at an evening party, the last of the three nights I was there, as singers and dancers of the neighborhood gathered together. During that lively evening, song and dance in the old style came back into actuality. And in that isolated district, such evening affairs were still a common and enjoyable experience.

Among the songs recorded there were: *C'est un petit cordonnier* (a little shoemaker, looking around for a sweetheart)—a dance with a chorus; *Mon doux berger, n'as-tu pas vu?*—a shepherd lyric song, in which the shepherd pines for his sweetheart and looks for her in the hills; *Ce sont les filles de Saint Constant* or *C'est l'amour qui les prend*—a paddling song with solo and chorus; *Isabeau s'y promène*—a lilting dance song about a girl on the seashore who is lured aboard a ship by passing sailors, falls asleep to their singsongs, and awakens too late to regain the shore.

This first harvest of folktales and folksongs lasted through the summer until it reached into the hundreds—200 folktales and nearly 600 songs. The search for more went on steadily through the following years. Collaborators joined in. They were Massicotte, Lambert, Godbout, Carrière, Brassard, Arsenault, Le Blanc, Dr. Gauthier, and others. Recitals and folksong and handicraft festivals marked the revival of folklore in the region until, after 1940, the universities in French Canada became interested. Scholars and students awakened to a new humanism based on the traditions of the people. Professor

Luc Lacourcière, Mgr. Félix-Antoine Savard, Madeleine Doyon, and Elizabeth Brandon began to collect on their own or under the sponsorship of the National Museum of Canada and the Archives de Folklore at Université Laval.

The Archives de Folklore were founded at Quebec. The growth of this kind of research in eastern Canada through the decades since 1915 would take too long to describe here in detail and can be found elsewhere. A total of well over 13,000 song texts had been reached in 1955, more than 7,000 of which with melodies are recorded on the phonograph or on tapes or by ear. And the work goes on yearly at a steady pace throughout the expanses of what used to be New France in North America—in Quebec, in Nova Scotia and New Brunswick, and along the Missouri and the Mississippi rivers as far as Louisiana.

# Jongleur Songs of Old Quebec

# LA BERGÈRE MUETTE

## *THE MUTE SHEPHERDESS*

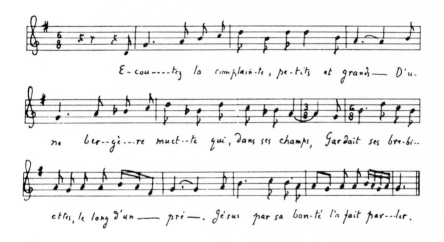

## La Bergère muette

Écoutez la complainte,   petits et grands,
D'une bergère muette   qui, dans ses champs,
Gardait ses brebi-ettes,   le long d'un pré.
Jésus par sa bonté   l'a fait parler.

Un jour, la sainte Vierge   lui est apparu'. (*bis*)
"Bonjour, joli' bergère,   grande Isabeau!
Voudrais-tu me donner   un des agneaux?"

"Ah non, certes!" dit-elle,   "sont pas à moi. (*bis*)
À mon père, à ma mère   j'en parlerai.
À mon père, à ma mère   je leur dirai."

3

Ell' s'en est retournée   bien promptement. (*bis*)
"Mon père, yat une dame   dans mon troupeau.
Grand Dieu! ell' me demande   un des agneaux."

Son père, aussi sa mère   fur' bien surpris (*bis*)
D'entendre la muette   parler ainsi.
À Dieu firent prière   qu'il ait merci.

"Va lui dire, ô bergère,   dans ton troupeau, (*bis*)
Qu'ils sont à son service,   grands et petits,
Que tous sont pour lui plaire,   jusqu'aux plus beaux."

La bergère, elle est morte   avant trois jours. (*bis*)
Ell' tenait une lettre   dedans sa main,
Ecrite du grand maître,   Dieu souverain.

Son père, aussi sa mère   n'ont jamais lu. (*bis*)
À fallu que l'archevêque   y soit venu
Parler à la muette,   grande Isabeau.

"Ouvre ta main, bergère,   ouvre ta main, (*bis*)
De la part du grand maître,   Dieu souverain!
A bien lu la lettre,   à bien compris."

Qu'en chante la complainte   le vendredi, (*bis*)
Gagne les indulgences,   le paradis. (*bis*)


## The Mute Shepherdess

Draw near, children of Mary, and I will tell
The sad tale of a shepherdess, mute from birth,
Till, through His Holy Mother, come down to earth,
Our Lord Jesus did make her to speak full well.

"A boon, shepherdess, surely you'll not deny:
One lamb out of your flock will you give to me?"
To her spoke Mother Mary full lovingly,
To which, finding her speech, did the maid reply:

"These sheep, beautiful Lady, are not my own,
I'll ask father and mother: O parents dear,
Now say, which of your lambs may I give to her
Who now in my affliction such grace has shown?"

But they, kneeling in pray'r, cried out, "Ev'ry one!
To Her for Her great mercy we give them all:
They're Hers just for the asking, both great and small,
As thanks from our full hearts for the wonder done."

Alas! soon it was willed that the maid should die.
No more on the high hills might she herd her sheep.
Her hand held firm a letter of myst'ry deep:
'Twas writ, yea it was sealed, by the Lord on High.

Alas! father nor mother could write nor read.
To them came the archbishop the words to tell;
He spoke in his great wisdom to Isabelle,
For none other than him would the dead maid heed.

"My child, open your fingers, unclasp your hand
And know this is the bidding of God most high
To tell what's written here, for His priest am I,
To all, that you may hearken and understand."

So here, children of Mary, is my advice:
To sing this tale each Friday with fast and prayer.
For this pardon and blessing I now declare,
And then life with the blessed in Paradise.


The Virgin's visitations on earth, as they are related in folksong,
are of varied descriptions. In her miraculous appearances at times she
rescues the faithful, shelters the innocent, punishes the guilty, and
foils the Devil. At other times she wanders about in beggar's guise,
like her divine Son, bestowing eternal reward or punishment for the
deed of hospitality granted or withheld. It is the former, the more
typical role, that she reveals in the above complainte of "The Mute
Shepherdess."

5

Popular recognition of this song, as vouched for by oral tradition, has been far wider in Canada and Acadia[1] than in the motherland. Compared with twenty-six records of it so far in the New World, it has come to our attention in only nine versions in the collections of old France: once from Gascony, once from Velay and Forez, three or four times from Nivernais, once from Provence, and in three numbers of the *Poèsies populaires de la France* (the Ampère collection), at the Bibliothèque Nationale.[2] All except a very few recorded versions in France and America being in pure French, it is evident that they belong to a province of *langue d'oïl*, probably somewhere on the Loire River. Of the only two Provençal records, one, that of Arbaud, clearly indicates a northern origin by its prosodic distortion and mixture of dialects—*langue d'oc* and *langue d'oïl*, southern and northern. La Muto in its Provençal form, for the first stanza, is:

> L'y avie' no bargeireto
> Que gard' au champ
> Uno tānt belo damo
> Li vai devant . . .

In the New World the twenty-six versions recorded belong half to Canada and half to Acadia, as can be seen in the list appended below. The majority of the early immigrants from France to Acadia and Canada were from the Loire River basin. And within Canada itself, or the valley of the Saint Lawrence, all its versions but one were collected below Quebec, the lone exception being Lambert's Berthier record (No. 4). This is due to a persistent difference between the Quebec (lower-river) and Montreal (upper-river) repertory; complaintes and cantilènes are far more common on the lower than on the upper Saint Lawrence.

---

[1] Canada, as part of ancient New France in North America, at first extended only from the lower Saint Lawrence up this river to Lake Ontario. Acadia, quite independently, was centered around the Bay of Fundy in what is now Nova Scotia and New Brunswick. That is why, down to the present day, the descendants of the early settlers in both parts still like to call themselves Canadians and Acadians (or Cayens).

[2] For Gascony, cf. Bladé, "La bergère mudo," *Poésies populaires de la Gascogne*, 1:177–181; for Velay and Forez see Smith, "La bergère muette," in *Romania*, No. 13, 110–112; for Nivernais, see A. Millien, *Chants et chansons populaires du Nivernais*, 1:57, 58; for Provence, see Arbaud, *Chants populaires de la Provence*, 2:53–55. See *Poésies populaires*, Nos. 107–110, "Complainte de la fille muette."

6

# REFERENCES AND SOURCES

**Published:**

1. Under the title of "The Dumb Shepherdess" in *Folk Songs of French Canada,* by Barbeau and Sapir, 81–86 (Bibliog. 14).

2. J. Bélanger and M. Barbeau, "La césure épique dans nos chansons populaires," *Les Archives de Folklore* 1:133–135, 149 (Bibliog. 60).

**Canadian and Acadian versions:**

1–3. In the Barbeau collection, National Museum of Canada: versions of Mme. Jean-F. Bouchard, Éboulements (Charlevoix), in 1916, No. 44; of Mme. Mathilde Audet, Éboulements-en-bas, 1916, No. 109; and of Mme. Aimé Simard, Saint-Irénée (Charlevoix), 1916, No. 188.

4. Collected by E. Z. Massicotte from Joseph Rousselle, Saint-Denis (Kamouraska), 1917, No. 1094.

5. Collected by the Rev. P. Arsenault at Mont Carmel, Prince Edward Island, *ca.* 1924; its melody was recorded by the Rev. Gallant.

6. Adélard Lambert, Berthier-en-haut, *ca.* 1917: "La Sourde-muette" (legend).

7. François Saint-Laurent, La Tourelle (Gaspé), in 1918, No. 2331.

8. Antoine Minville, Ruisseau-à-Patates (Gaspé), in 1918, No. 2446.

9. Mme. Joseph Levesque, La Tourelle (Gaspé), in 1918.

10. Mme. Zéphérin Dorion, an Acadian of Port-Daniel (Baie-de-Chaleur), in 1923, No. 3332.

11. Paul Langlois, Port-Daniel, in 1923.

12. Pierre Cronier "Klem," in the concession of Klemville at Port-Daniel, in 1922.

13. Mme. Ferdinand Langlois, of Klemville in Port-Daniel, of which she said, "It was learned by whoever worked in the lobster factory."

14. Collected by E. Z. Massicotte from Ephrem Dessureau at Sainte-Geneviève-de-Batiscan, No. 3120.

15. Copied from a notebook of Alfred Michel, Port-Daniel, dating back to 1906 and written at Grand'Mère (Quebec).

16. Communicated by Laurent Beaudry, Saint-Hyacinthe, *ca.* 1925.

17. Copied in 1925 from Mme. Pierre Dompierre's manuscript songbook at Saint-François-Nord (Island of Orleans).

18–23. In the J. T. Le Blanc Acadian collection, National Museum of Canada, *ca.* 1939: versions of Mme. Gaspard G. Saint-Pierre, Sheila, N. B.; of Mme. François Allain and Néré Richard, Saint Antoine, N. B.; Mme. Joseph Bordage, Saint Luc, N. B.; Mlle. Georgina Mazerolle, Saint Jean, N. B.; J. J. Comeau, Sheila, N. B.; and of Mlle.

7

Celina Leblanc, Montreal. These last six were published in *La Voix d'Evangéline,* a newspaper, Moncton, N. B.; December 21, 1939.

24. In the Barbeau collection, National Museum of Canada, from Mme. Ernest (Flavien Gagnon) Bouchard, Bergeronnes (Chicoutimi), in 1946, No. 5516.

25–27. In the Carmen Roy collection, National Museum of Canada, *ca.* 1948–1950: versions of Octave Minville, Saint-Joachim (Gaspé), No. 4890. Mme. Pierre E. Arbour, Percé (Gaspé), No. 5320; and Mlle. Angélique Parisé, Paspébiac (Gaspé), No. 5617.

28, 29. In the Luc Lacourcière and F. A. Savard collection, Archives de Folklore, Quebec: versions of Mme. Gautier, Saint-Irénée (Charlevoix), 1949, No. 892; and of Thomas Bouchard, Saint-Siméon (Charlevoix), 1946, No. 247.

30. In the Conrad Laforte collection, Archives de Folklore, Quebec, from Mme. Conrad Dallaire, Anse-Saint-Jean (Chicoutimi), 1955, No. L192.

31. In the Dr. Dominique Gauthier collection, Archives de Folklore, Quebec, from Mme. Pierrot Haché, Shippigan Gully, N. B., 1953, No. G341.

# OÙ VAS-TU, MON PETIT GARÇON?

## *WHERE BE GOING, LITTLE BOY?*

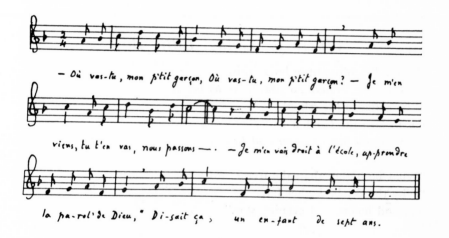

## Où vas-tu, mon petit garçon?

"Où vas-tu, mon p'tit garçon?" (*bis*)
  *Je m'en viens, tu t'en vas, nous passons.*
"Je m'en vais droit à l'école,
Apprendre la parol' de Dieu,"
  *Disait ça un enfant de sept ans.*

"Qu'est-c'qu'est plus haut que les arbres?" (*bis*)
"Le ciel est plus haut que l'arbre,
Le soleil au firmament."

9

"Qu'est-c'qu'est plus creux que la mer?" (*bis*)
"L'enfer est cent fois plus creux,
L'enfer aux feux éternels."

"Qu'est-c'qui pousse sur nos terres—" (*bis*)
"Les avoines et les blés d'or,
Les châtaignes et les poiriers."

"Que f'ras-tu quand tu s'ras grand?" (*bis*)
"Je cultiverai les champs,
Nourrirai femme et enfant."

## Where Be Going, Little Boy?

"Where be going, little boy?" (*bis*)
  *Here come I, here go you, there us be.*
"I be going to the school
For to larn the Golden Rule."
  *So a small boy of seven said to me.*

"What be higher than the trees?" (*bis*)
"Why the sky be higher far,
Sun and moon, and evening star."

"What be deeper than the sea?" (*bis*)
"Hell's a hundred times more deep
With the flames that never sleep."

"What be sprouting through the soil?" (*bis*)
"Why, the hay and golden wheat,
And the pears, and apples sweet."

"What may be the life you plan, when you grow to be a man?" (*bis*)
"Just a farmer man I'll be, with a wife and family."

Intended for childhood, this school song is unique. It was recorded only once, in Acadia (now Nova Scotia), and remains as elusive as the lesson it teaches. It is lofty like the tree whose profile is projected upon the sky, and deep like the sea. Yet it is as humanly poetic as the golden wheat fields swaying in the breeze. It ends up on a fatalistic note: when grown to manhood, the young singer will have, like others, to plow the fields and feed wife and children. In brief, the problem of life is presented here in a nutshell. The refrain whispers softly: "You come along, you go by, we all alike pass away." This lyric comment upon life hinges upon faith and evokes the tragic fate of the Acadian people, whose dispersion and misfortunes are the theme of Longfellow's *Evangeline,* and to whom it seems to belong exclusively, on a wild shore.

In spite of its having been recorded only once anywhere, so far as we know, it seems to have been composed by a singer of old France, for *châtaignes* and *poiriers* are not familiar in Acadia. Besides, this distinction marks its source as being in the motherland at a time when poetic tone and jongleur prosody were flourishing. Its lines count seven syllables, a feature found only in folk poetry. If feminine words in spots endeavor to match without rhymes masculine endings, it is due to the lapses which are common in oral transmission through the generations. Its refrain is in two halves, in each stanza, one half inside, and the other outside, at the end.

This song brings to mind another, of which only one stanza was recorded, and with a different tune and the interior refrain "Tirlanlire, tourlanloure." It belongs to the Massicotte collection at the National Museum and was found in the Montreal district. It runs as follows:

"Mon petit garçon, dis-moi, quel est ton nom?
  Ton nom et ton prénom?"
"Je suis l'enfant de mon père,
  *Tirlanlire,*
  *Tourlanlour,*
Aussi l'enfant de ma mère,
  *Tourlanlour,*
  *Mon gâ!"*

Compare this song with Child ballads #1 and # 46.

### REFERENCES AND SOURCES

**Published:**

1. Barbeau, *Alouette!,* 161–163 (Bibliog. 59).
2. Peggy Stack and Elizabeth Harding, *French Songs for Children* (Bibliog. 96).

**Sources:**

This song has been recorded only once, so far as is known, from the Rev. P. Arsenault, curate of Mont Carmel, Prince Edward Island, who learned it from his mother, and by the Rev. Théodore Gallant, curate of Sturgeon, who recorded the tune by ear. It was communicated to the author at the National Museum in 1924, together with a valuable collection of 120 other Acadian songs.

# LA COMPLAINTE DE CADIEUX

## *THE LAMENT OF CADIEUX*

## La Complainte de Cadieux

Petit rocher   de la haute montagne,
Je viens ici   finir cette campagne!
O doux échos,   entendez mes soupirs!
En languissant   je vais ici mourir.

13

Petits oiseaux,  vos douces harmonies,
Quand vous chantez,  me rattach' à la vie.
Ah! si j'avais  des ailes comme vous,
Je s'rais heureux  avant qu'il fût deux jours.

Seul en ces bois  que j'ai eu de soucis,
Pensant toujours  à mes si chers amis!
Qui me dira,  ah! sont-ils tous noyés?
Les Iroquois  les auraient-ils tués?

Par un beau jour  que, m'étant éloigné,
En revenant,  je vis une fumé',
Je me suis dit:  "Qu'est-ce qui loge ici?
Les Iroquois  m'ont-ils pris mon logis?"

Tout aussitôt,  je fus en embassade,
Afin de voir  si c'était embuscade.
J'ai aperçu  trois visages français,
M'ont mis le cœur  d'une trop grande joi'.

Mes genoux pli'nt,  ma faible voix s'arrête.
J'ai tombé là.  A partir ils s'apprêtent.
Je restai seul.  Pas un qui me consol'.
Quand la mort vient,  pas un ne s'y désol'.

Un loup hurlant  vint près de ma cabane
Voir si mon feu  n'avait plus de boucane.
Je lui ai dit:  "Retire-toi d'ici,
Car sur ma foi,  je perc'rai ton habit!"

Un noir corbeau,  volant à l'aventure,
Vint se percher  tout près de ma toiture.
Je lui ai dit:  "Mangeur de chair' humain',
Va-t'en chercher  autre viand' que la mienn'!"

Prends ta volé',  dans ces bois, ces marais.
Tu trouveras  plusieurs corps iroquois.
Tu trouveras  des tripes, aussi des os.
Mange à ton saoul!  Laisse-moi en repos!

14

Rossignolet,  va dire à ma maîtresse,
A mes enfants,  qu'un adieu je leur laisse,
Que j'ai gardé  mon amour et ma foi,
Que désormais,  faut renoncer à moi.

C'est aujourd'hui  que le mond' j'abandonne,
Mais j'ai recours  à vous, Sauveur des hommes.
Très Sainte Vierg',  ne m'abandonnez pas!
Permettez-moi  d'mourir entre vos bras!

## The Lament of Cadieux

Upon this rugged mountain top at last I seek repose.
The struggle and the strife of life are drawing to a close.
O gentle echo, hear my parting sigh,
For here I come to languish and to die.

As through these mountain solitudes I reach the summit high,
I see the happy-hearted birds to leafy shelter fly.
O joyous birds, if I had wings like you,
I'd hasten to my father's home anew.

Here in this wood remote I pine and hide a broken heart
From all the life-long friends I love like brothers torn apart.
Are all my dear ones drowned, alas! who knows,
Or murdered by our savage Indian foes?

Lo, and behold! A prowling wolf broke in on my repose,
Toward me drawn by scent of food that from my cabin rose.
"Begone forthwith, foul beast of prey," I cry,
"Or by my faith without delay you die."

A rav'n came hovering near, as black as black could be,
He perched himself upon my bed and croaked most dismally.
Fly to the marshes, seek your dinner there.
On Indian corpses you may richly fare!

15

O nightingale, I pray you haste unto my mistress dear!
I leave her my unbroken troth, the gage of love sincere.
For my last rest I choose this lonely spot.
Bid her farewell, bid her forget me not.


The epic adventures of Cadieux and his forerunner, Dollard des Ormeaux, on the Ottawa River are just two out of many episodes in the colonial wars that began with the discovery of Canada. Iroquois marauders soon attacked the French settlements on the eastern seaboard, even before Quebec was firmly established. The fur business and the rivalry between the white traders—French and Dutch—were the prime incentives in this conflict.

The benefits of the trade were the mainstay of the precarious settlements of the French on the Saint Lawrence, no less than of those of the Dutch at Manhatten (now New York) in New Holland and, a little later, at Albany, close to the Agniers (Iroquois) occupying the Mohawk River to the west. The beaver pelts were the produce of the nomadic Algonkin [1] tribes of the northern woodlands, and merchants, of whatever nationality, had to secure them from those wild hunters. As early as 1600, the Algonkin tribes of the Great Lakes to the west marshaled themselves into canoe brigades in order to convey safely their valuable fur bundles to the French merchants who had won their allegiance at an early date and had furnished them with the goods they coveted. The barter would have gone on peacefully had not the Dutch and their Iroquois confederates meddled with the northerners.

The main artery of this forest activity, after 1640, ran across Lake Nipissing, down the French and the Ottawa rivers. Every spring the hunters from the northwest, the Hurons of Ontario, and the French *coureurs de bois* paddled their way eastward in their canoe brigades, thus inviting the southern invaders to come and await them in ambush, on the Ottawa portages which favored their inroads.

Year after year this warfare of the borderlands proceeded mercilessly. In 1660 the whole Dollard party was massacred on the lower Ottawa. About fifty years later (*ca.* 1709) Cadieux and his family, while journeying down the upper Ottawa, detected the tracks of hostile rovers at Alumette Island. To save his canoe load, Cadieux

---

[1] The definition as adopted at the National Museum of Human History is that Algonkin is the general term applying to the whole stock, whereas Algonquin applies only to the tribe of the Ottawa River.

sent his family down the rapids, and stayed behind on the trail at the waterfalls to stalk the raiders and delay their pursuit. Here it is that the narrative of our complainte begins. Cadieux lost his life at the hands of the enemy and lived only long enough—so it is supposed—to write his death chant with his own blood on a sheet of birchbark, pin it with a thorn on a tree trunk, and bury himself by the trail with his own hands.

His death chant—actually composed by a survivor—was his memorial and has proved more enduring than stone and mortar. Tragedies of this type, according to immemorial custom, were the object of such heartfelt commemorations down almost to the present day in eastern Canada. The memory of Cadieux long survived him in the spoken tradition of the upper Ottawa and in his death chant or complainte. The author was the last of the historians who recorded them during the last hundred years. The earliest to do so was the distinguished German explorer, J. G. Kohl [2] who wrote, about 1850–1860:

> The old French Voyageur brought many a pretty song from France into these remote countries, and you may hear on the Upper Mississippi, and in the bays and wild rivers of Lake Superior, even at the present day, an old chanson sung two hundred years ago in Normandy, but now forgotten there. But I am not speaking here of that class of songs. . . . I here especially allude to the songs composed on the spot which are characteristic of the land and its inhabitants, as the people paint in them their daily adventures, themselves, and the surrounding nature. Among these poetic productions, there is much that makes no great figure in a book, although it produces its good effect in actual life. . . . Generally they designate their own most peculiar songs as "chansons de Voyageurs," and exclude from them songs they have derived from France and elsewhere. [In those Voyageur songs] I discovered a deeper poetical feeling. These are termed the "complaintes."

These complaintes, in themselves, are not thoroughly Canadian; they are a type of popular and elegiac romance well known in French literature. Still it is characteristic enough for land and people, that of all the numerous varieties of French songs, these complaintes should have found a local habitation and a name in Canada and on Lake Superior.

I heard the people speak of their complaintes everywhere, and I

---

[2] *Kitchi-Gami—Wanderings round Lake Superior*, London, 1860, 254, 259, 260–264.

am bound to believe that at least half of their songs consist of elegies. Indeed it may be fairly asserted that their entire music and poetry have an undercurrent of elegy.

Complaintes are often made about tragical events, especially shipwrecks and deadly accidents, which become universally known. One of the most celebrated of these elegies is that in which the melancholy fate of Jean Cayeux is lamented. It describes a thoroughly Canadian tragedy and is characteristic of the voyageurs and the country. This complainte is very long, and unfortunately I met no one who knew it at all by heart, though I took considerable trouble. But I heard many fragments at different places; nearly every voyageur knew a part of it, or was at least acquainted with its contents.

Jean Cayeux (according to the story) was a great Canadian voyageur, a hunter and fur trader, beloved by the Europeans and friendly Indians and known through the entire country of the Saint Lawrence. He was once voyaging and hunting on the Ottawa River and was stationed for a long time with his wife and children and all his family in the neighborhood of the cataracts known as *le Grand Calumet*. It was in the old French time, when the Iroquois, the partisans of the British, were still powerful and frequently made savage and extensive forays into the land. They would creep along forest paths and appear quite unexpectedly, like lightning from a clear sky, attacking the French settlements and those of their Indian allies; and if they were victorious, nothing escaped their merciless arms and fire. One evening Cayeux saw his camp surrounded and threatened by such a suddenly appearing band of Iroquois. He had nothing at hand but a canoe; in this his wife and children saved themselves, and his young son went to the stern to guide it. *"Généralement on ne saute pas le Grand Calumet,"* for [the rapids] are too violent, rocky, and long. Hence a portage is usually made; but Cayeux' family ventured it, as there was no other way to safety left them.

Cayeux himself remained behind, fearing lest he might overload the canoe and thus expose his family to certain death; but he promised to rejoin them by a circuitous route. Then he sprang on a rock in the center of the river and watched his family safely glide down the wild cataracts and float on to the smooth water below. He saw them commit themselves to the mercy of God and fold their hands in prayer. He saw, too, that a white form appeared on the bow of the canoe and recognized in her the Blessed Virgin. At length he saw them saved from the Indians, who had followed them like foxes along the bank. The pious family, under the protection of the Virgin, soon reached a part of the river where there was a strong French post which the Indians dared not attack. Then Cayeux began to think of his own safety, for the Iroquois, who quickly returned when their prey escaped them, were preparing to pursue him. Cayeux rushed into the woods, but his enemies soon cut off the road which would lead him to his family and drove him northward to the upper deserts of the Ottawa River. By day the fugitive Cayeux managed to conceal himself in hollow trees; at night he hurried on through the thickest scrub. The chase lasted for days, and still he heard the howling of the Indians after him. His provisions gradually gave out and his strength began to fail. Later, although the Iroquois, too, at length grew weary of the chase and returned to their own country unsuccessful, it was all over with poor Cayeux. They had driven him into such a wild, swampy, and remote desert that he no longer had the strength to find his way back from it to the inhabited parts of Canada and to his family. As a protection against rough weather, he built in his pathless desert a little hut of branches on the shore of one of the uppermost confluents of the Ottawa. This river was the only path that led into Canada, but he had no canoe to take advantage of it. Nor did he dare to venture forth from his hiding place, for he feared that he might yet fall into the hands of his enemies. His only hope was that Frenchmen would pass along the river and save him.

> C'est donc ici, que le monde m'abandonne,
> Sainte Vierge, ne m'abandonnez pas!

So runs the complainte. But no one visited him save the beasts of the forest. One day a wolf walked yawning past his body. "Ha! thou savage comrade, what wouldst thou?" Cayeux, who was now ill, shouted to the animal. "I am not yet completely broken. Take to flight, or thou must wrestle for the prize with me!" A croaking raven seated itself the next day on the branch of a nearby tree. *"Eh! mangeur de chair humaine!"* Cayeux addressed it. "Thou hast come to see how far I am gone. But see, I have still strength enough to drive thee away." And the raven flew off with a croak of disappointment. Cayeux grew weaker and weaker every hour, and when on the third day three little singing birds came and sat twittering before his hut, he began to lament and gave them a mournful message:

> Cher petit oiseau des érémites,
>   Va dire à ma maîtresse,
> Que les érémites ne pensent plus à moi.

19

He now felt that his hour had arrived and with the expenditure of his final strength dug himself a Christian grave. Over the grave he erected a cross and carved on the wood his complainte, the entire history of his tragic fate. (So, at least, my Canadians asserted. They believed they sang the very song composed by Cayeux on his deathbed.) As he lay there before his cross, and, dying, prayed, three French faces appeared before him.

## REFERENCES AND SOURCES

**Published:**

1–3. In the 1860s by pioneer folklorists of Quebec, F. A. H. LaRue, Joseph Charles Taché, Ernest Gagnon. Cf. *Journal of American Folklore* 67:167–168 (1954): versions classified according to the date of collection.

4. P. E. Prévost, *Chansons canadiennes*, 8, 9, under the title "Petit rocher de la haute montagne," which seems to have been borrowed from the Massicotte or Gagnon repertory (Bibliog. 6).

5. Cecilia Ray Berry, *Folk Songs of Old Vincennes*, 24, 25 (Bibliog. 64).

6. Barbeau in *Journal of American Folklore* 67:163–183 (1954) with 13 tunes, a dissertation, musical analysis, and a list of versions utilized in reconstructing the text accompanied by its variants (Bibliog. 93).

**Sources:**

The thirteen versions listed and utilized in the study of this Canadian complainte (Bibliog. 93) belong to the National Museum collection and were recorded from 1917 to 1951 by E. Z. Massicotte, the author, Joseph Thomas Le Blanc, François J. Brassard, and Mlle. Carmen Roy. These versions come from the Red River (Manitoba), old Vincennes (southern Indiana), the Ottawa River, Laprairie, Sainte-Geneviève-de-Batiscan, Berthier-en-haut, La Tuque, Temiscouata county, Cap-Chat, and Port-Daniel in the Gaspé Peninsula. Le Blanc's version, from Trocadie, New Brunswick, was published in the Moncton newspaper *La Voix d'Evangéline* in 1940.

At later dates the following versions were added to the collections of the National Museum, Ottawa, and to the Archives de Folklore, Quebec:

14, 15. Mlle. Carmen Roy recorded for the National Museum two more versions, one from Angélique Parisé, seventy-eight years old, Paspébiac, in 1950, No. 5640; the other is from Benoit Denis, Cap-Chat, in 1951, No. 6612.

16–18. The Luc Lacourcière collection at the Archives de Folklore, Quebec, contains three more versions, recorded after 1950: 16 is from Mlle. Bella Chiasson, Lamèque, N. B., No. 963; 17 is from Eustache Noël, Lamèque, N. B., 1950, No. 1043; and 18 is from Séraphic Duguay, Lamèque, N. B., in 1951, No. 1078.

# BLANCHE COMME LA NEIGE

## WHITE AS THE SNOW

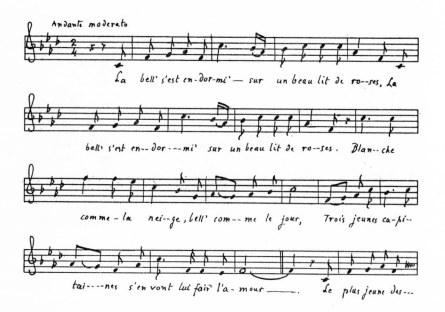

## Blanche comme la neige

La belle s'est endormi'   sur un beau lit de roses. (*bis*)
Blanche comme la neige,   bell' comme le jour,
Trois jeunes capitaines   s'en vont lui faire l'amour.

Le plus jeune des trois   la prend par sa main blanche. (*bis*)
"Montez, montez, princesse,   dessus mon cheval gris!
A Paris je vous mène   dans un fort beau logis."

Tout aussitôt rendus  a cette hôtellerie: (*bis*)
"Mangez, buvez, la belle,  selon votre appétit!
Avec un capitaine  vous passez la nuit."

Au milieu du repas,  la belle tombe morte. (*bis*)
"Sonnez, sonnez les cloches,  tambour au regiment!
Ma maîtresse, elle est morte,  à l'âge de quinze ans."

"Où l'enterrerons-nous,  cette aimable princesse?" (*bis*)
"Au jardin de son père,  dessous un pommier gris.
Nous prierons Dieu pour elle,  qu'elle aille en paradis."

Mais au bout de trois jours,  son père se promène, (*bis*)
"Ouvrez, ouvrez la tombe,  mon pèr', si vous m'aimez!
Trois jours j'ai fait la morte,  pour mon honneur garder."

## *White as the Snow*

The maiden lies asleep and soft her bed of roses, (*bis*)
Pure and white as a snowflake, and beautiful as day!
To her came three gallant captains to steal her heart away.

The youngest of the three her white hand took and kissed it. (*bis*)
"Mount and ride, lovely lady upon my good gray mare.
And to Paris we'll betake us, a home awaits you there."

Within a dwelling fine, he led that gentle maiden. (*bis*)
"Eat and drink, lovely lady! You'll learn to fancy me,
And beside your gallant captain the night will merry be."

But ere the feast was done, she died, that gentle maiden. (*bis*)
"Bells shall be tolled in the belfry, the muffled drums shall roll.
Dead, alas, lies youth and beauty, may heaven receive her soul."

"O where shall be her tomb, most gentle of princesses?" (*bis*)
"In her father's garden, beneath an apple tree.
We'll pray to God Almighty, her soul in heaven may be."

Her father three days hence was walking in his garden. (*bis*)
"Open the tomb, dear father! my dying was but feigned.
Three days I died, dear father, that I might live unstained."


Scholars are agreed [1] in their estimate of *White as the Snow* (*Blanche comme la neige* or *Celle qui fait la morte pour son honneur garder*) as one of the outstanding folk ballads in the French language. It has, indeed, seldom been equaled, in its genre, for poetic beauty.

A beautiful princess of feudal days is lured from her lovely bed of roses by the youngest of three roving knights. In the Paris hostelry where she is conveyed she drops dead in the middle of the feast. "Ring, oh, ring the bells!" The easily deceived, romantic men-at-arms kneel to an unlikely prayer and bury her under a gray apple tree in her father's garden. Three days later she rises from her grave to her father's arms, for she had "played the dead three days for the sake of purity." The unknown poet has in a few strokes conjured up such a graceful picture that his ideally unreal characters appeal to us somewhat like the quaint personages of an ancient Gobelin tapestry.

Of the popularity of *Blanche comme la neige* one may form an idea from the wide range of its diffusion and the favor it has found among singers of the past centuries. Folklorists have already compiled more than a hundred independent versions of it in France, Canada, northern Italy (Piedmont), Spain (Catalonia), and Switzerland.[2]

More remarkable still, it has passed into the Breton and Basque languages at the French frontiers. Scholars, too, have shown an unusual interest in this ballad. We may mention the controversy engaged in in the 1880s between C. Nigra, the noted Italian folklorist, and A. Loquin [3] on the debatable point of its original prosody, the brief, though pithy, analysis of Doncieux,[4] and the review by Jean

---

[1] Cf. Barbeau and Sapir, *Folk Songs of French Canada*, 40–41 (Bibliog. 14).

[2] About forty-five versions have been listed for France, chiefly by E. Rolland (*Recueil de chansons populaires*, vol. 3, 58–63); Decombe (*Chants et chansons populaires d'Ille-et-Vilaine*, 150–153); Doncieux (*Le Romancéro populaire de la France*, 269, 270); and A. Millien (*Chants et chansons populaires du Nivernais*, vol. 1, 222–228); eight for Italy, six of which are by Nigra. A. Rossat (*Publications de la société suisse des traditions populaires* 13(1917):68–72) has since found nine in French Switzerland; and about thirty versions have come to our notice in Canada since 1916. Several versions are also found in the Ampère manuscript collection at the Bibliothèque Nationale, Paris, under the title of *Poésies populaires de la France*.

[3] *Mélusine* 6:217–219.

[4] *Op. cit.*, 269–279.

Richepin [5] in which the poet sums up his remarks with the words, "On y trouve un grace incomparable et un rare élégance."

Well known as it is to folk singers in Quebec and Acadia—our collections hold about thirty records in northeastern Canada—it may seem strange that it did not come to the attention of educated Canadians until a few years ago, and that it is not to be found in their folksong anthologies. The text above cannot be considered either perfect or final, although some of the gaps in the individual versions have been filled in by comparing several of the available records.

## REFERENCES AND SOURCES

**Published:**

1. "Blanche comme la neige," in *Veillées du bon vieux temps,* 57–58 (Bibliog. 9).

2. "White as the Snow," in *Folk Songs of French Canada,* Barbeau and Sapir, 40–44 (Bibliog. 14).

3. "Dessous le laurier blanc," by W. A. Dorrance, *University of Missouri Studies,* 10, No. 2, 120–129: without the melody (Bibliog. 42).

4. "Dessous les lauriers blancs," by Marius Barbeau, *Les Archives de Folklore* 1:140, 141, 150.

5. "Blanche comme la neige" by Sœur Marie Ursule, *Les Archives de Folklore* 5–6:279, 280 (Bibliog 83).

6. "La fille du roi," in *Histoire et traditions de la paroisse des Avoyelles en Louisiane,* by Corinne Lelia Saucier, 430 (Bibliog. 73).

**Canadian and Acadian versions:**

1–6. In the author's collection, from Mme. Jean F. Bouchard, Éboulements, 1916 (melody reproduced here); from Mlle. Wilyémine Carrier, Sainte-Marie (Beauce), 1917, No. 1273; Magloire Savard, La Tourelle (Gaspé), 1918, No. 2219; Napoléon Jean, Saint-Antonin (Temiscouata), 1918, No. 1859; François Saint-Laurent, La Tourelle (Gaspé), 1918, No. 2117; François Dupuis, Chemin-Neuf (Gaspé), 1918, No. 2597.

7. In the Archange Godbout collection, *ca.* 1920, from Anatole Rainville, Saint-Edmond (Berthier).

8. In the same collection, from Mlle. Marie-Renée Giroux (Montreal), *ca.* 1920.

8a. Collected by E. Z. Massicotte, from V. F. de Repentigny in 1917, from Joseph Langevin, Saint-Timothée (Beauharnois), No. 869; published in *Veillées du bon vieux temps,* 56, 57 (Bibliog. 9).

---

[5] *Journal de l'Université des Annales,* 12e année, no. 5, 205.

9. In the collection of the Rev. P. Arsenault, the Rev. Gallant, Mont Carmel, Prince Edward Island, No. 27.

10. In the J. T. Le Blanc collection, National Museum of Canada, from the notebook of Mme. Annie Maillet, Waterville, Maine, No. 9464.

11–15. Also in the Acadian collection of J. T. Le Blanc, mostly published in *La Voix d'Evangéline,* Moncton, N. B.; from Mme. Joseph Lanteigne, Island River, N. B.; from Mme. Mélanson, N. B.; from Mme. Alex Robichaud, Bonsecours, N. B.; from Edmond F. P. Le Blanc, Cape Bald, N. B.; from Mme. Liboire Vautour, Leger Corner, N. B.

16. In the author's collection, from Mme. Onésime Lavoie, born at Saint-Irénée (Charlevoix); tune recorded by Mrs. Laura Boulton, New York, 1941.

17. In the collection of François Brassard, Jonquières (Chicoutimi), from Mme. Henri Fraser, No. 4702.

18. In the author's collection, from Mlle. Albina Guérin, 76-years old, Laprairie (Quebec), 1945.

19. In the collection of Luc Lacourcière and F. A. Savard, Archives de Folklore, Quebec, from Mme. Armand Bouchard, Baie-des-Rochers (Charlevoix), 1946. Phonog. 241.

20–26. In the Carmen Roy collection, National Museum of Canada, all from the Gaspé Peninsula, from Octave Minville, Saint-Joachim, Phonog. 4906; from Mme. Théodore Auclan, Rivière-à-Claude, Phonog. 4954; from Ernest Lemieux, Petite-Madeleine, Phonog. 5166; from L. Collins, Saint-Joachim, Phonog. 5159; from Mme. Pierre E. Arbour, Percé, Phonog. 5326; from the Acadian Mme. Zéphérin Dorion, Port-Daniel, in 1951, Phonog. 6713; from Mlle. Angélique Parisé, Paspébiac, in 1950, Phonog. 5692.

27. In the collection of Luc Lacourcière, from the Acadian Majorique Duguay, Petite-Lamèque, Shippigan, N. B., 1955, Phonog. 1176.

# LE PRINCE DES ORMEAUX

## *THE FAITHLESS BETROTHED*

- jo----li ber-ger —, chan-te-moi la chanson que tu chan-tais, en gardant tes mou-tons, que tu chan-tais —, en gardant tes mou-tons, en gar-dant tes — mou---tons. — Ah! oui, beau prince, je

## Le Prince des Ormeaux

"Joli berger,   chante-moi la chanson
Que tu chantais   en gardant tes moutons, (*bis*)
              En gardant tes moutons."

"Ah! oui, beau princ',   je vous la chanterai,
Mais j'ai grand peur   que vous soyez fâché, (*bis*)
              Que vous soyez fâché.

Car votre bell',   en filant ses amours,
Est accouché'   d'un fils, luy a trois jours. (*bis*)
              D'un fils, luy a trois jours."

27

"Si tu dis vrai,  de mon pain mangeras,
Mais si tu mens,  de ma main tu mourras, (*bis*)
                    De ma main tu mourras.

Bridez, sellez,  un de mes blancs chevaux
Que j'aille voir  m'ami' dans son château, (*bis*)
                    M'ami' dans son château."

Sa bonne mèr',  qui est dans les créneaux,
A vu venir  le prince des Ormeaux, (*bis*)
                    Le prince des Ormeaux.

"Ma chère fill',  quel jour infortuné!
Voilà ton princ'  qui vient pour t'épouser, (*bis*)
                    Qui vient pour t'épouser."

"Très chère mèr',  présentz-lui ma sœur,
Qui me ressembl'  de la bouche et des yeux, (*bis*)
                    De la bouche et des yeux."

"Bonjour, la bell',  que faites-vous ici!
Ce n'est pas vous  qu'il me faut aujourd'hui, (*bis*)
                    Qu'il me faut aujourd'hui.

C'est votre sœur  cent fois plus bell' que vous,
Celle qui port'  ma chaîne d'or au cou, (*bis*)
                    Ma chaîne d'or au cou."

"Hélas! ma fill',  ton malheur obstiné!
Voilà ton princ'; ta sœur a refusé, (*bis*)
                    Ta sœur a refusé."

"Très chère mère,  faut ouvrir mon écrin.
Apportez-moi  mon beau mouchoir de brin, (*bis*)
                    Mon beau mouchoir de brin.

Apportez-moi  mes beaux pendants dorés.
Devant mon princ',  je veux me présenter, (*bis*)
                    Je veux me présenter."

28

"Bonjour, m'ami', où sont tout' tes couleurs?
Dessous tes yeux   je vois de grand' douleurs, (*bis*)
             Je vois de grand' douleurs.

Ah! dis-moi donc, ah! dis-moi sans mentir,
Qui est le pèr',   le père de ton fils? (*bis*)
             Le père de ton fils?"

"Nenni, beau princ'!   Reprends tes anneaux d'or;
Dedans tes yeux   j'ai vu l'arrêt de mort, (*bis*)
             J'ai vu l'arrêt de mort."

A dégaîné   sa claire épée céans.
Trancha la têt',   mit la cervelle au vent, (*bis*)
             Mit la cervelle au vent.

"Sonnez trompett',   tambours au régiment!
C'est ma maîtress'   qui est morte à quinze ans, (*bis*)
             Qui est morte à quinze ans."


## The Faithless Betrothed

"Come, pretty maiden, sing me the song you sing,
The song you sing when you go shepherding, (*bis*)
             When you go shepherding."

"My gallant princeling, I fear that when I do,
That when I do, my song will sadden you, (*bis*)
             My song will sadden you.

Poor prince! Your lady, profuse of lovers gay,
Your lady gay a baby rocks today, (*bis*)
             A baby rocks today."

"If truth you tell me, you'll reap a rich reward,
If not, beware, beware my shining sword, (*bis*)
             Beware my shining sword.

Go bridle, saddle my charger snowy-white.
Her castle gate must welcome me tonight, (*bis*)
Must welcome me tonight."

Out on the bastion, her mother came to see.
"Your prince arrives and fast he rides, pardie, (*bis*)
And fast he rides, pardie!"

"Oh! mother, mother; let sister greet him well,
No eye so keen us two apart could tell, (*bis*)
Us two apart could tell."

"Good-day, my lady, what brings you here, I pray?
It is not you I'm looking for today, (*bis*)
I'm looking for today.

I seek your sister, a thousand times more fair,
Who that my chain, my chain of gold did wear, (*bis*)
My chain of gold did wear."

"Ill luck, my daughter, alas, your evil lot!
Your prince is here, your sister lures him not, (*bis*)
Your sister lures him not."

"Here bring my coffer, I prithee, mother mine,
For I must take therefrom my kerchief fine, (*bis*)
Therefrom my kerchief fine.

Dear mother, bring me my lace and jewels rare,
For I must greet my prince so debonair, (*bis*)
My prince so debonair."

"God greet you, maiden, say why so pale your cheek?
Your careworn eyes of pain and sorrow speak, (*bis*)
Of pain and sorrow speak.

Tell me, fair lady, of lying pray have done,
What man is he, the father of your son? (*bis*)
The father of your son?"

"Nay! all is over: take back your chain of gold,
For in your eyes my sentence I behold, *(bis)*
      My sentence I behold."

Forth from its scabbard he drew his shining sword,
His shining sword, but spoke to her no word, *(bis)*
      But spoke to her no word.

Showed he no mercy. Ah! pity 'twas to see,
With one fell stroke he slew her sans merci, *(bis)*
      He slew her sans merci.

"Sound forth, O trumpets and regimental drum!
To my false love let death full quickly come, *(bis)*
      Let death full quickly come!"

*Come, Pretty Shepherdess* is one of the outstanding complaintes in the French language. It stands on a par with *Marianson, Germaine,* and *Le roi Renaud.* Like them it is a manifestation of the epic genius of ancient France.[1]

Its form is both narrative and dialogued. Its dramatic beginning, its tense plot, and its somber ending all combine to make this story a real tragedy in spite of its relative brevity. The pastoral charm of its first line, "Come, pretty shepherdess, sing me the song . . ." turns to anguish as soon as the answer forecasts the news of infidelity. "But if yours is a lie," cries the prince, "from my own hand you shall pay!" Each verse thereafter marks a step toward the fatal curtain. Life or death is the stake.

This ballad no doubt commemorates the revenge of a medieval prince, as in *Marianson,* which it vaguely resembles. Had the art of telling been less, the bard might have produced only a gruesome tale; but his lofty inspiration and style saved the day.

Profound is the breath in the dialogue between the unfaithful princess and her mother, while the indignant husband is on his way home. "Dear mother, let my sister stand for me. . . ." "Alas! my daughter, your misfortune is beyond retrieve!" The prince on the doorstep cries out, "Ah! tell me without lying. . . ." "Nay, handsome

---

[1] Cf. the author's *Romancero du Canada,* 91–95 (Bibliog. 44).

prince! Take your golden rings back. I have seen my death warrant in your eyes." The head collapsed under his sword; her brain was scattered in the wind.

This song was not quite as well known in the motherland as in America. Our collections now contain at least twelve versions for Canada—only one from Acadia—whereas the overseas compilations do not contain more than half a dozen. Julien Tiersot in the past fifty years has written that he knew only two for France: one from Haute-Bretagne and the other from Normandy. But we have since discovered a few more French variants for Nivernais and Franche-Comté.[2]

Presumably it was known at one time all over France, for the few records preserved are widely scattered, from Brittany, where it seems to have originated, on to the Italian border which did not even stop its diffusion southward. One or two versions from Piedmont and northern Italy, quoted by Nigra, closely resemble those from Nivernais and Haute-Bretagne. And Brittany also possesses it.[3]

So this compainte belongs in common to three languages, Breton, French, and Italian, and it has taken root on two worlds, the Old and New. But the height of its popularity must have already passed at the time when America was discovered.

## REFERENCES AND SOURCES

**Published:**

1. Barbeau, *Romancero du Canada*, 91–95 (Bibliog. 44). Following an analytic study of this medieval song, a list of the versions recorded in Canada and Acadia is given, together with references to versions published in France, in Brittany, and Italy.

2. In "Civilisation traditionnelle des Lavalois," by Sœur Marie Ursule, *Les Archives de Folklore* 5–6:351, 352. No. 448 (Bibliog. 83).

**Canadian and Acadian versions:**

1–9. From the author's collection are listed (*op. cit.*) versions which were recorded in Beauharnois, at Pointe-Gatineau, Sainte-Famille (Île d'Orléans), La Tourelle (Gaspé), Penouille (Gaspé), Gascons (Baie-de-Chaleur), Port-Daniel (Gaspé).

---

[2] A. Millien, *Chants et chansons populaires du Nivernais*, 110–113; C. Beauquier, *Chansons populaires recueillies en Franche-Comté*, 255, 256.

[3] C. Nigra, *Canti popolari del Piemonte;* F. M. Luzel, *Gwerziou Breiz-Izel*, vol. 2, 7, 13, 559 (as mentioned by J. T. and Edgar Piguet).

10. "Joli berger, chante-moi la chanson," recorded by the author in collaboration with Mrs. Laura Boulton in 1941 from François Saint-Laurent and Joseph Ouellet, La Tourelle (Gaspé).

11. In the Carmen Roy collection, National Museum of Canada, from Mme. Zéphérin Dorion, Port-Daniel, in 1951, No. 6672.

12. In the collection of Sœur Marie Ursule (Bibliog. 83).

# L'HIRONDELLE, MESSAGÈRE DES AMOURS

## *THE SWALLOW, LOVE'S MESSENGER*

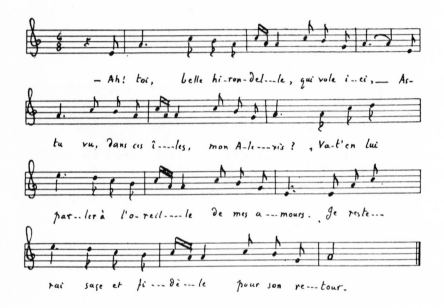

## L'Hirondelle, messagère des amours

"Ah toi, belle hirondelle   qui vole ici,
As-tu vu, dans ces îles,   mon Alexis?
Vas-t'en lui parler à l'oreille   de mes amours.
Je resterai sage et fidèle   pour son retour."

L'oiseau, qu'est tout aimable,   prit sa volé'.
Dans son léger plumage   s'est en allé,
Traversant les mers et les terres   sans s'y lasser.
Tout droit sur le mât du navire   s'est reposé.

34

L'aperçoit dans la hune   du bâtiment.
Alexis se lamente   en le voyant.
"Ne pleure pas, amant fidèle,   écoute-moi;
J'ai des compliments de ta belle   qui sont pour toi."

L'amant, plein de surprise · l'entend parler,
Reçoit bonnes nouvelles,   l'a salué:
"Ell' t'a donné son cœur en gage   et ses amours,
Ell' restera sage et fidèle   pour ton retour."

"Je te salu', la belle,   salut à toi!
Ton petit cœur en gage,   garde-le moi!
Je suis parti pour un voyage   dans les longs cours.
Je t'enverrai de mes nouvelles,   à mon retour."


## The Swallow, Love's Messenger

"O swallow, hovering around me   so gay and free,
Should you see my true lover,   greet him from me.
Into his ear, I bid you whisper,   tender and sweet,
I will be faithful to my darling,   till we shall meet."

The bird gentle and kindly   bade her goodbye;
On wings light and untrammeled   sped through the sky,
O'er land and sea tirelessly journeyed   following its quest,
Till on a mast softly alighting   sank down to rest.

And soon, looking around it,   sighted the lad,
Aloft high on the maintop   tearful and sad.
"Sorrow no more, O faithful lover!   Give ear to me!
Words of fond love from thy dear lady   bring I to thee."

The youth all these good tidings   joyfully heard.
"What more have you to tell me,   my bonny bird?"
"To love thee still she gives her promise,   your lady sweet;
She will be faithful to her lover,   until you meet."

35

"My heart, my faithful fair one,     thine own shall be,
And thine, I keep for ever,   it is for me.
I have a long journey before me   over the sea.
And all my news I'll tell thee darling,   when I meet thee."

The incoherence of this tale of pining love is not its least quality. *The Swallow, Love's Messenger* typifies a hoard of sentimental lyric utterances, in which the need of song to relieve pent-up feelings counts for more than the intellectual interest in the story. It is one of the most archaic songs of this collection, and its raggedness suggests the possibility that not a single line of its remote original may have remained intact.

The swallow as a messenger of love is the most important feature, for it is derived from the similar nightingale (*rossignolet*) theme of early days. The *rossignolet*, indeed, appears as the consoler and messenger of aggrieved lovers in the earliest French literature. It is of frequent occurrence in the troubadour manuscripts of the twelfth- and thirteenth-century period. Its ten-syllable line with cæsuras after the sixth syllable (6f + 4), once familiar to the troubadours, is uncommon in folk poetry. Doncieux failed to notice it in any of the folksongs that came under his observation. The only instance given in his *Romancéro* of the twelve-syllable lines (8 + 4) in the second halves of our stanzas is that of *Dame Lombarde*, a ballad from northern Italy and Piemont.[1]

*The Swallow, Love's Messenger,* even in its present adulterated form, is of French extraction. Versions of it are to be found in such distant parts of Quebec as Lévis, Montreal, and Gaspé. But we can as yet cite only two fragments of it from abroad, in Beauquier's Franche-Comté compilation. Of the feathered-messenger theme alone, however, several variants have been recorded in the French provinces. Bujeaud has given several instances of the "joli rossignol volage, messager des amoureux," of the "rossignolet sauvage, rossignolet charmant," which he obtained in the Loire River provinces. In Champfleury and Wekerlin, the rossignolette takes flight and conveys a spoken message to the pretty sweetheart. From the French Pyrenees, far to the south, several parallels are given by Julien Tiersot, in his *Chansons populaires des Alpes françaises.*[2]

---

1 George Doncieux, *Le Romancéro populaire de France,* xvi (footnote).

2 Beauquier, *Chansons populaires recueillies en Franche-Comté,* 87, 88, 371; J. Bujeaud, *Chants et chansons populaires des provinces de l'ouest,* vol. 2, 172, 232, 233; Champfleury and Wekerlin, *Chansons populaires des provinces de France,* 118,

## REFERENCES AND SOURCES

**Published:**

1. Barbeau and Massicotte, *Journal of American Folklore* 32:40–42 (Bibliog. 10).

2. Under the title of "The Swallow, Messenger of Love" in *Folk Songs of French Canada*, Barbeau and Sapir, 187–191 (Bibliog. 14).

3. *Romancero du Canada*, "L'hirondelle, messagère des amours," 135–138 (Bibliog. 44).

4. "C'était une belle hirondelle" in *Les Archives de Folklore* 1:132, 133, 149 (Bibliog. 60).

**Canadian and Acadian versions:**

1–8. Eight versions are listed in the author's *Romancero*, 137, 138; they are from Montreal, Beauharnois, Sainte-Famille (Île d'Orléans), Saint-Paschal (Charlevoix), Echouerie and La Tourelle (Gaspé), Caplan (Bonaventure), and Mont Carmel (Prince Edward Island).
At least six other versions have been recorded since 1937:

9. By François Brassard, from Urbain Petit at Strickland, Ontario, in 1943.

10. By J. T. Le Blanc, from Louisa Doucet, Robertville, N. B., *ca.* 1940, published in *La Voix d'Evangéline*, Moncton, No. 10096.

11. By Carmen Roy, from Damase Minville, Ruisseau-Arbour (Gaspé), No. 4952.

12. By Carmen Roy, from Joseph Robison, Anse-Pleureuse (Gaspé), No. 5338.

13. By Carmen Roy, in 1951, from Mlle. Angélique Parisé, Paspébiac, No. 6727. "C'est une fille de quinze ans," No. 6727.

14. By Luc Lacourcière, "Hélène est dans sa chambre," from Majorique Duguay, at Petite-Lamèque, Shippigan, N. B., 1952, No. 1223.

---

119; and Julien Tiersot, *Chansons populaires des Alpes françaises*, 120, 135, 348. Tiersot also mentions another version from Morvan.

# L'HERBE VERDIT TOUS LES PRINTEMPS

## THE FLOWERS COME EVERY SPRING

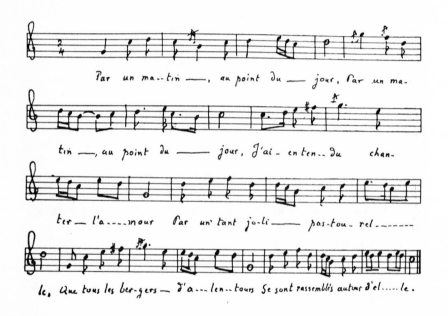

## L'Herbe verdit, tous les printemps

Par un matin, au point du jour, (*bis*)
J'ai entendu chanter l'amour
Par un' tant joli' pastourelle
Que tous les bergers d'alentours
Se sont rassemblés autour d'elle.

38

En voyant sa rare beauté, (*bis*)
D'elle je me suis approché.
Je me suis approché d'elle,
En lui disant: "Je suis berger.
Prends-moi pour ton amant fidèle!"

La belle répond d'un air doux: (*bis*)
"Petit badin, retirez-vous!
Moi, je suis pastourelle sage.
Si vous n'étiez pas si jaloux,
Je vous aimerais davantage."

"La bell', si j'ai perdu mon temps, (*bis*)
En cherchant bien, j'en trouv'rai autant,
Une autre que vous, aussi belle.
L'herbe verdit tous les printemps;
Les fleurs aux champs s'y renouvellent."


## *The Flowers Come Every Spring*

Early one morning at dawning of day, (*bis*)
Such a song of love I heard upon my way
By a most entrancing shepherd maiden.
Then all the shepherds sang a roundelay,
Off'ring her their hands with flowers laden.

Viewing her beauty beyond all compare, (*bis*)
I drew near and told her, told her then and there,
"I pursue the shepherd's simple calling.
Pray give ear while I my passion true declare:
I adore you, shepherdess enthralling!"

Then my proud beauty did coyly reply, (*bis*)
"Sir, you waste your time, your suit I do deny;
Maids like me may not be treated lightly.

39

Were you not so jealous, peradventure I
Might agree to treat you more politely."

"Maiden, I'm wasting my time, I agree. (*bis*)
Many million fish are left in the sea;
I shall thrive despite your airs and graces.
What though ev'ry year the flowers faded be,
Next year other blooms will take their places."

This is an *aubade* or a song at dawn, under the high window of the sweet beloved, in a world of romantic shepherds.

This one shepherd might have won a favorable reception had he not been so jealous. No sooner is he invited to withdraw than he cannot hide his spite. Burning the bridges behind him, he boasts at once that he can find as good if not better luck. Whoever listens might be annoyed at finding him so unchivalrous. But the offender's rashness is easily pardoned because of the two concluding lines of the song:

> *L'herbe verdit tous les printemps,*
> *Les fleurs aux champs se renouvellent.*

The prosody of this composition betrays its source, which is troubadourian rather than rustic (jongleur). Yet it belongs to the folk repertory under the dual caption of *aubade* (love song of dawn) and *pastourelle*. Its lines of eight beats (*pieds*) run into a stanza of five lines altogether, with rhymes at first masculine, then crossed, half of them feminine. This feature brings the type within the range of school and manuscript. Exchanges at the time were quite likely, if not frequent. And the remote origin of the pastourelle remains shrouded in mystery. Was it at first of high rank or lowly and of the folk?

The tune in A major, with colorful rests here and there (on *notes de passage*), assumes a modal character which confers upon it an irrestible charm. And its slightly syncopated rhythm enhances the beauty of its profile, in a panorama of fresh flowers, wherein shepherds, love-sick, whisper their desires into the reedy pipes of melancholy.

## REFERENCES AND SOURCES

**Published:**

Barbeau, *Alouette!*, 111–113 (Bibliog. 59).

**Canadian versions:**

Nine versions are listed in detail above; they were recorded along the Saint Lawrence by the author and his collaborator, E. Z. Massicotte, from 1918 to 1925. None have been found since, or elsewhere. They are from Montreal, Valleyfield, Sainte-Geneviève-de-Batiscan, Sainte-Famille (Île d'Orléans), Éboulements, Temiscouata, Sainte-Anne-des-Monts, and La Tourelle (Gaspé).

# VOILÀ LA RÉCOMPENSE

## *MUST I ENTREAT IN VAIN?*

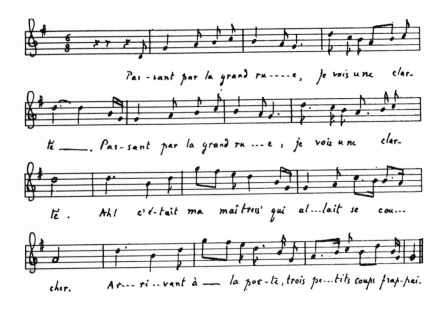

Pas-sant par la grand ru----e, je vois une clar-té ____. Pas-sant par la grand ru ---e, je vois une clar-té. Ah! c'é-tait ma maîtres' qui al...lait se cou... cher. Ar---ti--vant à ── la por-te, trois pe...tits coups frap-pai.

## Voilà la récompense

Passant par la grand rue,   je vois une clarté. (*bis*)
Ah! c'était ma maîtresse   qui allait se coucher.
Arrivant à la porte,   trois petits coups frappai.

Arrivant à la porte,    trois petits coups frappai (*bis*)
"Ouvrez, ouvrez la porte,   la bell', c'est votre amant
Qui revient de la guerre   dans un beau bâtiment."

"Je n'ouvre pas ma porte;  il est minuit sonné. (*bis*)
Mon père, aussi ma mère,  ils sont partis veiller.
Ils ont barré les portes,  ont apporté les clefs."

"Je vais à la fenêtre;  bell', me l'ouvrirez-vous? (*bis*)
Je suis couvert de neige,  dans l'eau jusqu'aux genoux.
Voilà la récompense  que je reçois de vous!"

"Les manteaux de mon père  sont dans les chambr's d'en haut. (*bis*)
Attendez un quart d'heure;  j'irai vous les chercher.
Sur votre épaul', beau prince,  je vous les y mettrai."

## *Must I Entreat in Vain?*

As I came through the city,  glimm'ring light I spied. (*bis*)
'Twas from my lady's casement,  her shadow passed inside.
Three times I tapped on her door,  the catch I gently tried.

I tapped thrice on her portal,  tapped so carefully. (*bis*)
"Open thy door, beloved,  love is calling thee.
I am your soldier lover  come home from across the sea."

"My door I cannot open,  midnight's far too near, (*bis*)
Father and mother are sleeping,  sleeping sound, my dear.
My door is locked and bolted,  the keys are hid, I fear."

"Then pray open thy window,  must I entreat in vain? (*bis*)
For I am cold and weary,  cold with snow and rain,
Oh! how have I deserved it,  that thou should'st me disdain!"

"Warm cloaks of fur has my father,  robes of velvet too. (*bis*)
Wait there for just a moment,  I'll fetch them down for you.
I'll wrap them round  and round you, my prince of lovers true."

This poignant song takes a dramatic turn, but its incentive is purely lyrical, like that of most love songs. Here a pretty girl encounters a

43

wanderer, who sighs at her window and aspires to be her lover. From the street below he sees her light above, her candle light; she is retiring for the night. He knocks at the door, "Open, will you?" He has just come back from the battlefields, if she would believe him. Here he stands benumbed, ankle-deep in the snow. "Nay!" she answers. "Midnight is rung; the doors are locked and bolted." Nowhere could she find the keys. In spite of this, the suitor bitterly complains. His fate is unfair. But the lofty one plays her role, calls him "handsome prince!" and offers to lay her father's coat on his arms, which are stretched out.

This type of composition is no novelty, nor is the song by any means of recent date. Nothing else in the lyric repertory of France is as ancient an heirloom. *Must I Entreat in Vain?* belongs to the class of love songs that goes back to the *lingua vulgaris (langue vulgaire)* of French literature in the eleventh century. It is a serenade; the gallant knight, according to a familiar pattern still surviving in Spain, stands under the window of his beloved, and his plea is that she must let him climb up to her, not only on the wing of his muse, but literally, via the stairway to her room.

This formula would be too rigid if it did not permit exceptions— for instance, sometimes the door chances to be ajar or the parents are still out. Availing themselves of their good luck, the young lovers often hear the midnight call of the town crier afar, or entranced, they linger together until the lark warns them of approaching dawn.

Whenever the poet of old sings of their love, his song is called an *aubade,* or *alba* in Spanish. This archaic form bears on the parting of lovers at the break of day. Jeanroy, in his *Origines de la poésie lyrique,*[1] asserts that once it was equally familiar in France, Germany, Italy, Portugal, and Spain.

But here we have to do with a subtype, the nocturne. The gallant knight appears at midnight, that is, bedtime. His feet may be soaking wet or not, it does not matter; he is wasting his efforts.

The song *Violà la récompense* on an ancient theme is known in New France as well as in the motherland, and also beyond the border, in northern Italy.[2] The versions recorded in Canada and Acadia— thirteen in all—belong to the collections of the author, E. Z. Massicotte, and J. T. Le Blanc. They cover a vast territory, from Batiscan up the Saint Lawrence, to Chaleur Bay on the Gaspé Peninsula, and down into New Brunswick. In France fewer versions are available, but they

---

[1] *Les Origines de la poésie lyrique en France, du moyen âge,* 46, 60, 76.
[2] Cf. the references in the author's *Romancero du Canada,* 115, 116 (Bibliog. 44).

are scattered over a wide area, in Ille-et-Vilaine, Calvados, elsewhere in Normandy, in Gascony to the south, and at Mézières to the east. It has even invaded northern Italy.[3]

The prosodic form follows the jongleur tradition. Its pattern is 6 + 6f, with feminine rhymes in twos or threes, and epic cæsuras—the mute there being uttered. The stanzas consist of tercets, three lines each. This is in the folk manner; the first of these lines is repeated. The tune is modal, in C with the tonic on G.

## REFERENCES AND SOURCES

**Published:**

Barbeau, *Romancero du Canada,* 113–116 (Bibliog. 44).

**Sources:**

The detailed list of eight Canadian and Acadian versions is given in *Romancero* above. These versions were recorded by E. Z. Massicotte and the author between 1920 and 1923. They are from Sainte-Geneviève-de-Batiscan, Sainte-Famille and Argentenay (Île d'Orléans), Saint-Denis (Kamouraska), La Tourelle (Gaspé), and Port-Daniel—two versions—in Baie-de-Chaleur.

Five more versions were recorded by J. T. Le Blanc and published in *La Voix d'Evangéline* in the Acadian province of New Brunswick, as follows: from Mme. François Allain, Saint-Antoine, N. B., No. 9526, at the National Museum; from Mme. Anthony Melanson, Memramcook West, N. B., No. 9525; from Philippe Gaudet, Moncton, N. B., No. 9527; from Mme. Liboire Vautour, Leger Corner, N. B., No. 9529; from Mme. Thomas Gauvin, Saint-Anselme, N. B., No. 9530.

---

[3] T. F. Crane, *Chansons populaires de la France,* 274; and C. Nigra, *Canti popolari del Piemonte,* 389.

# LE CŒUR DE MA BIEN-AIMÉE

## *THE HEART OF MY WELL-BELOVED*

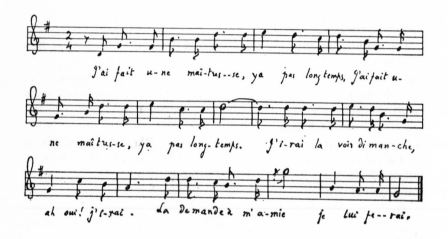

J'ai fait u-ne maî-trus--se, y a pas long temps, J'ai fait u-
ne maî-trus-se, y a pas long-temps. J'i-rai la voir di-man-che,
ah oui! j'i-rai. La demande à m'a--mie je lui fe--rai,

### Le Cœur de ma bien-aimée

J'ai fait une maîtresse,   y a pas longtemps. (*bis*)
J'irai la voir dimanche,   ah oui, j'irai!
La demande à m'ami'   je lui ferai.

"Si tu y viens dimanche,   je n'y s'rai pas. (*bis*)
Je me mettrai anguille,   sous un rocher.
De moi tu n'auras pas   mes amitiés."

"Si tu te mets anguille,   sous un rocher, (*bis*)
Je me mettrai pêcheure,   pour te pêcher.
Je pêcherai le cœur   d'ma bien-aimé'."

46

"Si tu te mets pêcheure,   pour me pêcher, (*bis*)
Je me mettrai gazelle,   dedans un champ.
De moi tu n'auras pas   d'contentement."

"Si tu te mets gazelle,   dedans un champ, (*bis*)
Je me mettrai chasseure,   pour te chasser.
Je chasserai le cœur   d'ma bien-aimé'."

"Si tu te mets chasseure,   pour me chasser, (*bis*)
Je me mettrai nonette,   dans un couvent.
De moi tu n'auras pas   d'contentement."

"Si tu te mets nonette,   dans un couvent, (*bis*)
Je me mettrai prêcheure,   pour te prêcher.
Je prêcherai le cœur   d'ma bien-aimé'."

"Si tu te mets prêcheure,   pour me prêcher, (*bis*)
Je me mettrai étoile,   au firmament.
De moi tu n'auras pas   d'contentement."

"Si tu te mets étoile,   au firmament, (*bis*)
Je me mettrai nuage,   pour te cacher.
Je cacherai le cœur   d'ma bien-aimé'."

"Si tu te mets nuage,   pour me cacher, (*bis*)
Je me mettrai en vierge,   au paradis.
De moi tu n'auras pas   d'contentement."

"Si tu te mets en vierge,   au paradis, (*bis*)
Je me mettrai saint Pierre,   j'aurai les clefs.
Et j'ouvrirai le cœur   d'ma bien-aimé'."


## The Heart of My Well-Beloved

A gentle lady charmed me, not long ago. (*bis*)
I'll visit her on Sunday; it shall be so,
I'll make my lady fair say "yes" or "no."

47

"But if you come on Sunday, I'll not be there. (*bis*)
Beneath a rock half-hidden I'd be an eel,
Your wish would not be gained. No love I'd feel."

"If as an eel you're hidden, under a rock, (*bis*)
Then I shall be an angler, angling for you.
I'll angle for your heart till it prove true."

"If you become an angler angling for me, (*bis*)
I'll be a little roe deer roaming the land,
And though you seek my love, you'll seek in vain."

"If you become a roe deer, roaming the land, (*bis*)
I'll chase you as a hunter over the plain,
Until I come at last your heart to gain."

"If you become a hunter scouring the plain, (*bis*)
A nun inside a convent cloistered I'll be.
Then certainly you'll taste no joy of me."

"A nun inside a convent if you become, (*bis*)
Then I'll become a preacher, preaching to you.
I'll preach and teach your heart how love is true."

"If you become a preacher, preaching to me (*bis*)
I'll be a star in heaven, lost in the blue.
Where I can never give comfort to you."

"Were you a star in heaven, lost in the blue, (*bis*)
I'd be a little cloudlet covering you,
I'd whisper in your heart, how love is true."

"Were you a little cloudlet covering me, (*bis*)
To Paradise I'd hide me, unmated yet,
And still in spite of all, no joy you'd get."

"Though Paradise receive you, unmated yet, (*bis*)
Then I shall be Saint Peter, I'll take my key
And I'll unlock your heart, then you'd love me."

48

The iteration of the same poetic pattern in every stanza of this song produces a distinctive cadence that craves continuity. The problems confronting the pursuer who would not be outwitted by the clever evasions of his well-beloved soon arouse a deep human interest. For beauty and originality *The Heart of My Well-Beloved* is not easily excelled; combining lucidity, economy of means, and youthful feeling, it ranks among the most beautiful lyric poems in the whole folk repertory of France.

When one of its earliest recorded versions (from the Aix district) was produced before the *Comité de la langue,* appointed by the French government in the fifties to save the folksongs of France, it provoked a lively debate, as some members, suspecting deceit, would not believe in its folk extraction. But time and the general consensus have brought accord. Mistral, the Provençal poet, knew it from infancy and by his paraphrase of it in the "Magali" of *Mirèio* brought it to fame among the literary classes. That at least another poet before Mistral yielded to its charm becomes apparent in a Provençal record of "Magali" from Avignon. Parts of this variant show traces of undoubted literary elaboration, in the following lines:

> O Magali, si tu te fais
> La rose belle,
> Je me ferai, moi, le papillon.
> Je te baiserai.

Or again,

> O Magali, si tu te fais
> L'arbre des mornes,
> Je me ferai, moi, la touffe de lierre.
> Je t'embrasserai.

If recognition from men of letters came late to *The Heart of My Well-Beloved,* the humble folk within and beyond the frontiers of France have for generations held it as one of their treasured possessions. Records of it, either in outline or in its present form, have come to us from varied sources and under different names, such as *Les Métamorphoses, Magali, Les Transformations,* and so forth. Arbaud stated that it was very well known in Provence; Rolland included three texts of it from Brittany in his *Recueil de chansons populaires;* H. Gaidoz introduced one from Carcassonne in *Mélusine* and men-

49

tioned that to his knowledge variants of the *Métamorphoses* had appeared in several languages. Parallels from Morbihan, Bourbonnais, Savoy, and Languedoc were produced by other authors. Bladé appended to his Gascon version several references to French and foreign sources, among which we note a record from Catalonia (Spain), one in Latin from the Engadine, and another from Rumania. Further variants of *Les Métamorphoses* were compiled by Jeanroy, in his *Les Origines de la poésie lyrique en France,* for instance, a few from Italy —Tuscany, Sicily, and south of Rome. To these T. F. Crane added two or three numbers; he mentions Nigra's versions for Italy and Child's *The Two Magicians,* where there is "a list of the two classes of popular tales containing the theme of our ballad." Arbaud also reminds us that Victor Leclerc had attempted to trace the song back to Anacreon.[1]

*The Heart of My Well-Beloved* has also been popular in New France, from Quebec, Acadia, Ontario, Ohio, down to Louisiana. Indeed, it is one of the most widespread in the French repertory in America. In the 1860s three of its versions were recorded in Quebec by Hubert LaRue and Ernest Gagnon, and it appeared in an early compilation entitled *Recueil de Chansons canadiennes et françaises,* 68–69. It has been published since, in Canada, Acadia, and Louisiana, more than twelve times (see Bibliography). Its recordings number at least twenty, of which eight are Acadian and three are from Louisiana. The present text was taken down in 1918 at Notre-Dame-du-Portage, from an old singer named Alcide Léveillé.

The prosody here belongs to the old-fashioned pattern: 6f + 4.

## REFERENCES AND SOURCES

**Published:**

1. First in Canada by Hubert LaRue, "Les Chansons populaires et les Iroquois du Canada," *Le Foyer canadien* 1:352 (Bibliog. 1). The same version was reproduced in *Le Canard,* Montreal, in 1897.

2. Ernest Gagnon, *Chansons populaires du Canada,* 137–141 (Bibliog. 2).

3. Julien Tiersot, *Songs of the People,* 23–25 (Bibliog. 7).

4. Barbeau and Sapir, *Folk Songs of French Canada,* "The Heart of My Well-Beloved" (Bibliog. 14).

5. Conrad Gauthier, "40 chansons d'autrefois"; two variants, 42–43, 82–83 (Bibliog. 38).

---

[1] For references, cf. Barbeau and Sapir, *Folk Songs of French Canada,* 198–200 (Bibliog. 14).

6. Irène Thérèse Whitfield, *Louisiana French Folk Songs*, 34–36 (Bibliog. 47).

7. Cecilia Ray Berry, *Folk Songs of Old Vincennes;* two variants, 42, 43, 64, 65 (Bibliog. 64).

8. Barbeau, *Alouette!*, "Le cœur de ma bien-aimée," 118–121 (Bibliog. 59).

9. Père Anselme et Frère Daniel, *Chansons d'Acadie* (Bibliog. 69).

10. Père Germain Lemieux, s.j., *Folklore Franco-Ontarien*, 12, 13 (Bibliog. 74).

11. Corinne Lelia Saucier, *Histoire et traditions de la paroisse des Avoyelles en Louisiane*, 428, 429 (Bibliog. 73).

12. Bélanger and Barbeau, *Les Archives de Folklore* 1:136, 137, 150 (Bibliog. 60).

13. Sœur Marie Ursule, "Civilisation traditionnelle des Lavalois," in *Les Archives de Folklore* 5–6:295, 296 (Bibliog. 83).

**Sources:**

1. Recorded by the author in 1918 from Alcide Léveillé, Portage (Temiscouata); reproduced in *Alouette!*, 119–121.

2. From Wilbrod Lavoie, Saint-Urbain (Charlevoix) in 1937, No. 4088.

3. In the Acadian collection of J. T. Le Blanc, from Joseph Caissie, of Cap-des-Caissies, N. B., No. 9765, at the National Museum.

4. From Mme. Edouard Noël, Sainte-Rose, N. B., in the "Chansonnier de Famille," No. 9766.

5. From Mme. Joseph Bordage, *ibid.*, Moncton, N. B., No. 9764.

6. Another version, *ibid.*, No. 9763.

7. From Eusèbe Thurbide, an Acadian living in Quebec, from Havre-aux-Maisons, Île Madeleine, in 1947 (melody recorded by Luc Lacourcière, Archives de Folklore, Quebec).

8. From Zoël Jonfe, another Acadian from the same island, Archives de Folklore, Quebec. It is sung by two singers, man and woman, in a duet.

9. Collected by Carmen Roy, *ca.* 1950, from Octave Minville, La Tourelle (Gaspé), No. 5074.

10. Luc Lacourcière, from Thérèse Pedneault and Jeannine Castonguay, in 1948, at Île aux Coudres (Charlevoix), No. 510.

11. From Laurent and Blanche Perron, on the same island, in 1948, No. 571.

12. Gaston Eugène Adam, as recorded in his manuscript thesis "Chansons françaises en Louisiane," 1944–1950.

13. Luc Lacourcière, from Joseph Jean, Shippigan, N. B., in 1950, No. 951.

14. ———, from Mme. Alfred Chiasson, Île Shippigan, N. B., in 1952, No. 1187.

15. Dr. Dominique Gauthier, from Mme. Patrick Godin, Évangeline, Gloucester, N. B., in 1952.

16. ———, from Léandre Savoie, same locality, 1952, No. G.45.

17. J. O. Ducasse, from Augustin Gallant, Saint-Alexis (Matapédia), in 1954, No. D.86.

18. Luc Lacourcière, from Florent Lemay, Lotbinière Co., Quebec, in 1955, No. 2743.

19. Mme. Elizabeth Brandon, in her manuscript thesis at Université Laval, *Mœurs et langage de la paroisse de Vermillon en Louisiane,* 84, 85 (Bibliog. 101).

# MON CŒUR EST À VOUS

## IRIS, YOU ARE AN ANGEL

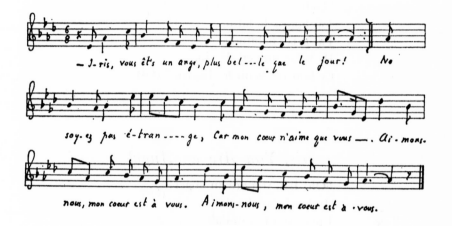

## Mon cœur est à vous

"Iris, vous êt's un ange,
Plus belle que le jour! } (bis)
Ne soyez pas étrange,
Car mon cœur n'aime que vous.
Aimons-nous, mon cœur est à vous." (bis)

"Mais, dans le voisinage,
Le monde le prétend, } (bis)
Vous êt's, amant volage,
Sujet au changement.
Beau galant, vous êt's inconstant." (bis)

53

"Laissez jaser le monde,⎤ (bis)
O ma rare beauté!          ⎦
Connaissez ma personne,
Avant que de parler.
Soulagez mon cœur attristé!" (bis)

"Là-bas, dedans ces plaines,⎤ (bis)
A retenti un chant.            ⎦
C'est la voix de maraine,
Qui s'écrie hautement:
'Ton amant vire à tous les vents!'" (bis)

"Là-haut, dans mes études,⎤ (bis)
J'ai appris le latin.          ⎦
J'ai pris l'habitude
De boire un ver' de vin.
Ce bon vin bénit le chagrin." (bis)


## Iris, You Are an Angel

"Oh! Iris, you are an angel⎤ (bis)
As lovely as the day.         ⎦
I pray you not disdain me,
My heart is yours alway.
Let's be lovers, don't say me nay." (bis)

"But when the neighbors gossip,⎤ (bis)
They all seem to agree            ⎦
That you're a lover flighty
As any lover can be.
You are fickle they all of them say." (bis)

"So let the blockheads babble,⎤ (bis)
My sweet dear little maid.        ⎦
Pray get to know me better
Before your last word's said.
Ease my sorrowing heart, I pray." (bis)

"I hear my old godmother ⎫ *(bis)*
Confound the cross old dear! ⎭
She wanders through the meadow,
Cries out for all to hear:
'You're in love with a faithless jay.' " *(bis)*


"When I was just a schoolboy ⎫ *(bis)*
I joined the Latin class; ⎭
But now I've learned much better,
I've learned to lift my glass.
Drink will chivvy dull care away." *(bis)*


Although French-born, this dialogue song (*à répons*) has been recorded only once anywhere so far as we know, that is, on the Island
of Orleans near Quebec. It brings face to face the lover, with his vows
of love, and Iris who rebukes him for his inconstancy. The repartee
of the suitor shows a literary distinction; this is due to his vanity in
the use of Latin. But he protests in vain; his beloved is not in the
least impressed. The flighty one abruptly gets off his high horse and
for consolation turns to a cup of sparkling wine. This expedient,
thanks to Bacchus, is quite familiar to disappointed lovers; it leaves
them free to try a hand at the same game elsewhere.

The last stanza, opening the door to libations, makes of this quar-
rel in courtship a lyric poem of a special type—a bacchic or drinking
song.

This composition, on a noble tune in the classic vein, is more subtle
than the common. No doubt it has departed from a school  of folk
variety, and its prosody is not entirely unsophisticated. The feminine
and masculine endings of its rhymes alternate, and its first lines are
satisfied with four to six syllables or beats, whereas the last swells up
to eight, as if for a final bouquet.

The air is in C major, in modern style, that this girl-teaser sings,
and he receives his refusal on the same chord.


## REFERENCES AND SOURCES

A single version of this song so far, has been recorded, from Mme.
J. B. Leblond at Sainte-Famille (Island of Orleans), by the author, in
1925. It was published with the melody in *Alouette!*, 126–128 (Bibliog. 59).

# CATIN, AIMABLE CATIN

## DOLLY, DEAR DOLLY

- Ca-tin —, ai-ma-ble Catin, Que fais-tu, Dans-ton jar-din ?

- Je — cueil' Des fleurs De mille cou-leurs Pour mon ser-vi-teur —. Je

veux bien en-faire un présent A mon fi---dèle a-mant.

### Catin, aimable Catin

"Catin, aimable Catin,
Que fais-tu dans ton jardin?" } *(bis)*
  "Je cueille des fleurs
  De mille couleurs
  Pour mon serviteur.
Je veux bien en faire un présent
  À mon fidèle amant."

"Ne veux-tu pas me donner
Quelques-un's de tes girofflées?" } *(bis)*

56

"Dedans mon jardin
Vous en choisirez
De ces beaux œillets.
Ils sont jolis, ils sont tous prêts
Pour un amant parfait."

"La bell' ne sont pas tes fleurs ⎤
Qui ont sû charmer mon cœur. ⎦ *(bis)*
    Ce sont tes beaux yeux,
    Tout brillants de feux,
    Me rend'nt amoureux.
Ne voudrais-tu pas en ce jour,
    Me donner tes amours?"

"Monsieur, les dam's à la cour ⎤
Accompliront vos amours.    ⎦ *(bis)*
    Moi, je suis sans biens;
    Pour mon entretien
    Ne possédant rien.
Voudriez-vous donc épouser
    La fill' d'un jardinier?"

"Ah oui, je t'épouserai,       ⎤
La bell', si tu veux m'aimer. ⎦ *(bis)*
    Cet anneau d'argent
    Vaut bien mille francs.
    Je t'en fais présent.
Je te ferai dame d'honneur,
    La femm' d'un gros seigneur."

"Adieu, mon joli jardin!        ⎤
Faut que je te quitte à présent. ⎦ *(bis)*
    Je m'en vais enfin
    Suivre mon amant,
    Quel contentement!
Pour être une dame d'honneur,
    La femm' d'un gros seigneur!"

# Dolly, Dear Dolly

"Oh! Dolly, dear Dolly, I pray,
What grows in your garden fair to-day?" } *(bis)*
"Flowers galore for one you see
Who follows me faithfully.
I gather blossoms of every hue
   To please my lover true."

"Oh! If I might have two or three;
Those sweet gilliflowers would welcome be." } *(bis)*
"From my garden, for my sake,
Carnations you may take,
For what so good as a fragrant clove
   To crown a perfect love?"

"Fair maiden, there's never a flower
Whose beauty to charm my heart has power. } *(bis)*
Eyes so bright with radiant light
Have charmed my fancy quite.
A boon I crave, all boons above;
   Oh! Grant me love for love."

"Dear sir, to the dames of the court
To favor your suit you should resort. } *(bis)*
Sir, you'd better pass me by.
No penny of dower have I.
My gentle sir, 'tis a fancy wild
   To marry the gardener's child."

"To you, little maid, I incline,
If only you'll say you deign to be mine. } *(bis)*
See, dear heart, this silver ring
For token of troth I bring.
A dame of honor 'twill make of thee,
  A lady of high degree."

"Adieu, pretty garden, adieu!
Forever today I part with you. } *(bis)*

I love him and he loves me.
I follow him joyfully.
A dame of honor I now shall be,
    A lady of high degree."


This song uses the term "dolly" (*catin*) only in an archaic sense, that of "country girl." In her ingenuous charm she does not lack naïveté. She frankly considers herself a gardner's daughter in the presence of a courtier who dangles a purse and rings the coins. Other dollies, especially the shrewd shepherdesses, would have protested indignantly. They would have castigated the gallant knight; they would have threatened him with their crooks.

But this pretty gardener, as soon as she sees her gilliflowers picked up and her carnations gathered, readily falls to this perfect lover. She turns toward him amorous glances (*tout brillants de feux*). Who knows! Even a gold-braided suitor at times may lose his epaulets for having pressed his gallantry a bit too far in the gardens along his path. Other songs elsewhere have glossed over such *mésalliances*. Country girls more than once have entered gilded halls, there to become maids of honor or wives of noblemen.

The long stanzas of this poem, the sophisticated and varied masculine rhymes, in pairs or triplets, and especially the intricate lines of seven, five, eight, and six syllables—particularly the fives and sevens— place it among the productions of the jongleurs, rather than of the troubadours.

This creation clearly belongs to the borderland, that is, it is either oral in its inception in the jongleur style, or it imitates the manner of the learned troubadours who recorded their poems with quills on parchment. Besides, we must not forget that the card makers and dealers in imagery were already at an early date producing broadsheets for a penny. Their influence on folksong makers in the fifteenth and sixteenth centuries was not negligible.

The charming melody which supports its lines and refined rhythm recalls the viola tunes and the harpsichord of bewigged musicians whom this pretty girl mentions, when she objects: "Sir, the ladies of the court may respond to your advances." Her graceful modulation, in the second phrase, repeats the same rigmarole; and it all seems to belong to the salons hung with tapestries, where color and subtlety are tenderly matched and are the delight of perfect lovers.

Unknown in the published collections until lately, this song was

59

nonetheless quite widely diffused among the folk of New France, that is of Acadia, Canada, and Louisiana, as may be seen in the list that follows.

## REFERENCES AND SOURCES

**Published:**

1. Barbeau, *Alouette!*, 122–125 (Bibliog. 59).

2. Sœur Marie Ursule, "Civilisation traditionnelle des Lavalois," *Les Archives de Folklore* 5–6:303 (Bibliog. 83).

3, 4. Corinne Lelia Saucier, *Histoire et traditions de la paroisse des Avoyelles en Louisiane*, 429; two versions (Bibliog. 73).

**Sources:**

*Acadian versions:*

1, 2. In the Acadian collection of the Rev. P. Arsenault and Rev. Gallant of Mont Carmel, Prince Edward Island, 1924, at the National Museum. This version only has been utilized here.

3–7. In the Acadian collection of J. T. Le Blanc of Moncton, N. B., at the National Museum, *ca.* 1940. His versions came from: (1) an Acadian woman in Kent Co.; (2) Mme. Léon Le Blanc, Fitchburg, Mass., and Mme. Marie Robichaud of Moncton, N. B.; (3) Mme. John Le Blanc of Hartford, Conn.; (4) Mme. Joseph Bordage of Saint Luc, N. B.; (5) Mme. Léo Mazerolle, Saint Léolin, N. B.; (6) Mrs. MacGould of Lakeburn near Moncton, N. B.

*Canadian versions:*

7. In Jules Tremblay's collection, National Museum, *ca.* 1920. This version was collected in the Eastern Townships, Quebec.

8–10. In the same collection there is a version from Montreal, where it was known and sung for generations in the Sénécal family; one from Stoke and Baie-du-Fèvre, Quebec, known in the Biron family; and one from the Carter family in Ottawa, who came from Sorel, Quebec. It is said also to have been sung at Sainte-Victoire, Quebec.

# C'EST LÀ MON DOUX PLAISIR

## *THERE IS MY SWEET JOY*

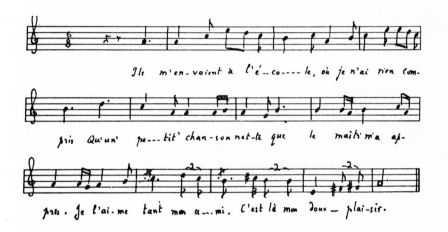

## C'est là mon doux plaisir

Ils m'envoient à l'école   où je n'ai rien compris
Qu'un' petit' chansonnette   que le maîtr' m'a appris.

*Je l'aime tant, mon ami,*
*C'est là mon doux plaisir.*

Un soir que je la chante,   mon papa m'entendit:
"Que dites-vous, ma fille,   il vous faut un mari?

Quand on les marie jeune   il faut bien les vêtir,
Il faut qu'on leur achète   robe de satin gris."

"Adieu, père, adieu, mère, adieu, tous mes amis!
Je m'en vais en ménage  avec mon cher mari.

Je bouillerai la soupe,  mettrai la poule au gril,
Je balaierai la place  et je ferai mon lit."


## There Is My Sweet Joy

They sent me off to school, they did,
Where I learnt ne'er a thing
Except a little ditty which
The master made me sing:

*I love my fav'rite boy.*
*He is my only joy.*

One night when I was singing it,
My father heard the tune.
"What's that you sing, my daughter,
You need a husband soon?

When little ladies marry young,
You must remember, pray,
You have to clothe the little dears
In silks and satins gray."

"Oh, I can boil delicious soup,
And grill a fowl all right,
And tidy up my happy home,
And make the bed at night."


This song has been recorded only once in both Canada and old France. It was sung by Mme. Jean "Français" Bouchard, the best singer of complaintes and come-all-ye's, in Charlevoix county. A woman's chant, it was meant for weddings; the last stanzas make this plain.

Many newlyweds must have used it at the banquet table, shedding a tear or two. "Good-by, all my friends! Now I am leaving for my own home." Married life, should we believe her, brought "more care than pleasure." "I'll boil the soup, sweep the floor clean." But the refrain breaks into a smile, as frequently it does: "I love him so much, my friend! It's my true pleasure!"

So gracious a song no doubt did not confine itself to the marriage rites. It could as well serve for household labors, either in front of the fireplace, or while spinning and weaving, and in the many other tasks which housekeepers of old would lighten with a tune.

Mme. Bouchard herself was a mother and a housekeeper at the head of a family. While her husband, the beadle at the parish church and a storyteller, lighted the candles at the altar or entertained the folk at an evening party, she boiled the soup, as in her song, and swept the floor clean. Through her kitchen window on the heights she could see Île aux Coudres (Hazel Island) sitting in the midst of the great river, and farther still, on a clear day, she could just perceive the rolling and wooded hills of the remote south shore of the Saint Lawrence.

Turning to the left, she would remember her birthplace, at Cap-aux-Oies (Goose Cape), in a small bay enclosed within a semicircle of majestic cliffs. There she had spent her childhood, singing: "When they are married young, they must have a dress of gray satin." In those days there was no railroad along the north shore in Charlevoix. The folk existed as in the early times, isolated on small farms, self-sufficient and contented, some of them owning a little sloop. Many songs were known, by her as by others. Her voice was rather thin, but how melancholy! She brought forth a number of quaint and beautiful ballads and also lively tordions for the dance. She had learned most of them from her father, Cyprien Perron (he knew a great many more), and from her aunt Philomène, who remembered a great deal of the past.

In those songs which she gave, ten or fifteen at a single sitting, the author—still early in his career as a folklorist—found inspiration and incentive to enlarge his collection. They were quaint and old-fashioned, they were novel and entrancing as music and poetry. *Gilère, La Fille dans la tour* (The Princess in the Tower), *Le Roi at une fille* (The King Has a Daughter), *La Bergère muette* (The Mute Shepherdess), and many others bring back a past age shrouded in legend.

After having taken down in shorthand and on the phonograph a score each day, plus a few folktales, the author evolved an effective plan for exploring the old folk traditions of Quebec to the core. Following his first discoveries of modal and syncopated melodies he became enchanted with the repertory, just as would another in old France or England when beholding the old carvings on the Gothic churches of the motherland, e.g., those of Chartres, Caen, or Bayeux, where the oral traditions of French Canada were born. Even the feeble voice of an aging singer whose hair was silvery gave a pale reality to the people in the songs or tales, as shadows confer high relief upon the stone profiles on the walls of medieval cathedrals.

## REFERENCES AND SOURCES

This song was, so far as is known, recorded only once, and by the author, from Mme. Jean F. Bouchard, in 1916. It is here reproduced.

It was included in the author's *Romancero du Canada,* 159–161 (Bibliog. 44).

Add

# LES FILLES À MARIER

## THE MARRIAGEABLE MAIDENS

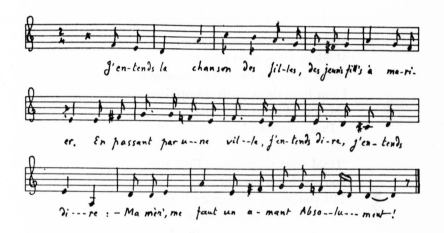

## Les Filles à marier

J'entends la chanson des filles,   des jeun's fill's à marier.
En passant par une ville   j'entends dire, j'entends dire:
  "Ma mèr', me faut un amant
    Absolument!"

"Tais-toi donc, petite sotte,   tu n'as pas encore quinze ans.
Un' jeun' fille de ton âge   doit êtr' sage et rester sage,
  Jusqu'à l'âge de vingt ans,
    Sans amant.

"Tiens, ma fill', voilà la somme   pour te conduire au couvent."
"Oui, ma mèr', de cette somme   je m'achèterai un homme.
　　Mon cœur sera bien plus content
　　　Qu'au couvent."


"Tiens, ma fille, voilà la route   pour te conduire au couvent."
"Oui, ma mèr', voici la mienne   qui m'y mène et m'en ramène
　　Dans les bras de mon amant,
　　　Qui m'attend!"


## The Marriageable Maidens

Maidens here are sweetly singing,
Maidens longing to be wed.
Slowly through the village strolling,
I can hear them softly whisp'ring,
"Mother, I must wed today.
　　Don't say nay!"

"Hold your tongue, you little silly,
You are hardly yet fifteen;
Till you're old enough to marry,
Love must tarry, love must tarry.
Till you're sixteen, you must be
　　Fancy free.

Here is money, O my daughter!
To the convent you must go."
"What a dowry this would make me!
Do not to the convent take me,
Let me find my love today,
　　Don't say nay!"

"Now my daughter, mine's the right way.
To the convent you must go."

66

"No, my mother, here is my way,
Right before me lies the highway
Leading to him, to my beau,
    Don't say no!"

All the *maumarié* songs of France put together—and they are many
—would not have changed this willful girl's determination to have her
own way and marry her lover without waiting another day. Not even
her mother's rebukes would have led her to believe that she was still
too young to be chattering this twaddle, for fifteen years of age was,
to the knowledge of all, the proper age for matrimony!

This debate between mother and daughter found its way into various songs familiar in France and elsewhere. But it assumes here the
garb of a spinning song, particularly as to its melody and rhythm.
Widely known in Old World lore as is our theme,[1] it does not in-
variably appear archaic in its treatment. Yet the present song conforms to a jongleur prosodic pattern 7f + 7 (the cæsura being feminine or epic), which belongs to the romance dialects and languages
of the *midi,* including Spain. Its diffusion shows that it prevailed in
the south and was little known in the north. In France its few versions come from Franche-Comté and Savoie, that is, from the *langue
d'oc* provinces.[2]

In New France, although it was recorded a few times along the
Saint Lawrence and in Gaspé Nord, it is far more widespread in
Acadia, as may be seen in the list below. As the Acadians were originally Poitevins, from south of the estuary of the Loire River, we may
conclude that on both sides of the Atlantic *Les Filles à marier* was
predominantly a song of the south, whose focus radiated northwest-
ward.

## REFERENCES AND SOURCES

**Recorded and published:**

Sœur Marie Ursule, in her thesis "Civilisation traditionnelle des
Lavalois," *Les Archives de Folklore* 5–6:291, No. 425 (Bibliog. 83).

---

[1] Cf. Barbeau and Sapir, *Folk Songs of French Canada,* 207 (Bibliog. 14).
[2] C. Beauquier, *Chansons populaires recueillies en Franche-Comté,* 228, 229;
C. Servettaz, *Chants et chansons de la Savoie,* 176, 179; and Estella Canziani, *Customs, Traditions, and Songs of Savoy,* 80, 81.

**Sources:**

1. Recorded by E. Z. Massicotte in 1920, from Émile Vaillancourt of Montreal, who learned it from M. Bélanger at Labelle.

2. Recorded by Massicotte from Amédée Lemay, who learned it from his mother, Dalida Morasse, of Cap-Santé (Portneuf).

3. Recorded by the author in 1925 from Mme. J. B. Leblond, Sainte-Famille (Île d'Orléans), No. 3196.

4. From J. Lemieux, in a notebook in 1930, who learned it from Joseph Beaubien, Cap-Chat (Gaspé).

5. From Mme. Zéphérin Dorion, an Acadian, at Port-Daniel (Bonaventure) in 1923, No. 3373. Here reproduced.

6. From Mme. Octave Dorion, who learned it about 1875 from Paul Laviolette, who came from Quebec City, No. 3491.

7. In the J. T. Le Blanc Acadian collection at the National Museum, from Mme. François Allain, Saint Antoine, N. B.; published in *La Voix d'Évangéline,* No. 9125.

8. From a manuscript of Eva Jean, *ibid.,* No. 9126.

9. From Joseph Bordage, Saint Luc, N. B., *ibid.,* No. 9127.

10–12. Collected by Carmen Roy in 1950 from Mme. Zéphérin Dorion, Port-Daniel, No. 5821; in 1950 from Leon Collins, La Tourelle (Gaspé), No. 5588; and from Mme. Pierre E. Arbour, Percé (Gaspé), No. 5369.

# JE VOUDRAIS M'Y MARIER

## I WANT TO GET MARRIED

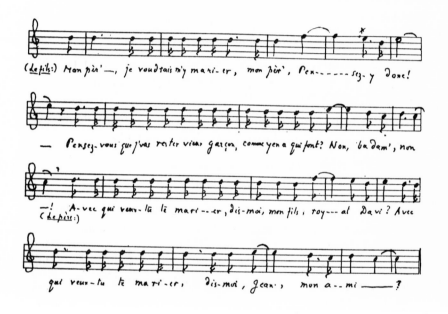

## Je voudrais m'y marier

"Mon pèr', je voudrais m'y marier,  mon pèr', pensez-y donc!
Pensez-vous que j'vas rester vieux garçon,

> *Comme y en a qui font?*
> *Non, badam', non!"*

"Avec qui veux-tu te marier, dis-moi,  mon fils, royal Davi'?
Avec qui veux-tu te marier,  dis-moi, Jean, mon ami?"

"Avec la plus bell' fill'  que j' pourrai trouver, mon pèr', pensez-y donc!
Pensez-vous que j'vas marier un ratafia,

> *Comme y en a qui font?*
> *Non, badam', non!"*

"Avec quoi gageras-tu ta femm'  dis-moi, mon fils, royal Davi'?
Avec quoi gageras-tu ta femm',  dis-moi, Jean, mon ami?"

"Avec des bell' bagues et des beaux joncs,  mon pèr', pensez-y donc!
Pensez-vous que j'vas la gager  avec un jonc d'cuivre,

> *Comme y en a qui font?*
> *Non, badam', non!"*

"Avec quoi habill'ras-tu ta femm',  dis-moi, mon fils, royal Davi'?
Avec quoi habill'ras-tu ta femm',  dis-moi, Jean, mon ami?"

"Avec d' la bell' soie, du beau satin,  mon pèr', pensez-y donc!
Pensez-vous que j'vas l'habiller  avec d' la cotonnad',

> *Comme y en a qui font?*
> *Non, badam', non!"*

"Avec quoi nourriras-tu ta femm',  dis-moi, mon fils, royal Davi'?
Avec quoi nourriras-tu ta femm',  dis-moi, Jean, mon ami?"

"Avec d' la bonne sauciss', du bon jambon,  mon pèr', pensez-y donc!
Pensez-vous que j'vas la nourrir  au foie d' mouton,

> *Comme y en a qui font?*
> *Non, badam', non!"*

"Sur quoi couch'ras-tu ta femm',  dis-moi, mon fils, royal Davi'?
Sur quoi couch'ras-tu ta femm',  dis-moi, Jean, mon ami?"

"Dans une bell' couchett',  sur un bon lit d'plume.
Pensez-vous que j'vas la coucher  sur une couchett' canayenne,

> *Comme y en a qui font?*
> *Non, badam', non!"*

70

# I Want to Get Married

"Father, the time has come for me to get married, father,

*What do you say?*

Do you think that I'm going to remain a bachelor, though others may?

*Nay, father, nay!*"

"With what sort of a girl do you want to be married? Now, my son,

*Pray answer me!*

With what sort of a girl do you want to be married? Say, John,

*Who will it be?*"

"With the most beautiful girl I can find, father,

*What do you say?*

Do you think that I'm going to marry a cheap baggage, though others may?

*Nay, father, nay!*"

"With what sort of a ring will you wed your wife? Now, my son,

*Pray answer me!*

With what sort of a ring will you wed your wife? Say, John,

*What will it be?*"

"With a very fine ring and a keeper, father,

*What do you say?*

Do you think I'm going to give her a ring of brass, though others may?

*Nay, father, nay!*"

"With what sort of stuff will you dress you wife? Now, my son,

*Pray answer me!*

With what sort of stuff will you dress your wife? Say, John,

*What will it be?*"

"With the very finest silk and satin, father,

*What do you say?*

Do you think that I'm going to dress her in cheap cotton, though others may?

*Nay, father, nay!"*

"With what sort of food will you feed your wife? Now, my son,

*Pray answer me!*

With what sort of food will you feed your wife? Say, John,

*What will it be?"*


"With thick slices of ham and rich sausage, father,

*What do you say?*

Do you think I'm going to feed her on sheep's liver, though others may?

*Nay, father, nay!"*

"On what sort of a bed will you lay your wife, my son?

*Pray answer me!*

On what sort of a bed will you lay your wife? Say, John,

*What will it be?"*


"On a beautiful bed with a mattress of down, father,

*What do you say?*

Do you think that I'm going to bed her on a shake-down of straw, though others may?

*Nay, father, nay!"*


In this song it is the young man who pleads with his father, rather than the daughter with her mother, to get on with the wedding without the loss of another day. It is usually called *Les Vêpres* or *L'Air des vêpres* because its tune is that of the psalm "In exitu Israel." It is the 7th Psalm Tone (with 6th ending). It is done under the form of a debate, a man and a woman standing opposite each other in the lively repartee.

That it is known in France the author has been assured by a representative of Musée des Traditions populaires. It is also a favorite in some parts of Quebec, but not, apparently, in Acadia or Louisiana.

## REFERENCES AND SOURCES

**Published:**

1. Barbeau, *Veillées du bon vieux temps,* 35, 36. As sung in 1917 by L. H. Cantin of Lévis, and Vincent Ferrier de Repentigny, formerly of Beauharnois, it was called *Air des vêpres* (Bibliog. 9).

2. Conrad Gautier, "40 Chansons d'autrefois," 18, 19 (Bibliog. 38).

**Sources:**

1. Recorded in 1941 from Omer and David Ouellet, at Saint-Croix (Rimouski) and entitled *Royal David.*

2. By Conrad Laforte, at Baie-Sainte-Catherine (Saguenay), from Louis Henri Pupont in 1955 for the Archives de Folklore, No. L208.

3. By Luc Lacourcière from Damase Gaudet, at Sainte-Emilie (Lotbinière), in 1955. It was called *Les Vêpres.*

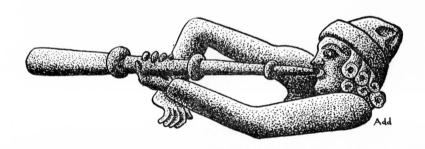

# CORBLEUR, MARION!

## *CORBLEU, MARION!*

## Corbleur, Marion!

(*Lui:*)   *Morbleur, sambleur, Marion!*
    Où étais-tu,   hier au soir?
          *Sambleur!*
    Où étais-tu,   hier au soir?
          *Corbleur!*

(*Elle:*)   Ah! Jésus, mon mari!
    J'étais allée   à la fontaine,
          *Mon Dieu!*
    Pour y laver   tes bas de laine,
          *Seigneur!*

(*Lui:*)  *Morbleur, sambleur, Marion!*
    Est-c'que ça prend une semaine . . .
    Pour y laver des bas de laine? . . .
(*Elle:*) . . . Mais la fontaine était brouillée. . . . (*bis*)

(*Lui:*) . . . Qui avait brouillé la fontaine? . . . (*bis*)
(*Elle:*) . . . Ce sont les chevaux de la reine. . . . (*bis*)
       (*ou:*

    Ce sont les cavaliers de Rennes).

(*Lui:*) . . . Ces cavaliers, j'voudrais les voir. . . . (*bis*)
(*Elle:*) . . . Ils ont passé le ventr' à terre. . . . (*bis*)

(*Lui:*) . . . A qui était la claire épée . . .
    Qu'était plantée dans le plancher? . . .
(*Elle:*) . . . Ce n'était pas un' claire épée, . . .
    C'était ma quenouille à filer. . . .

(*Lui:*) . . . A qui était cet habit rouge . . .
    Qui était près de la ch'minée? . . .
(*Elle:*) . . . Ce n'était pas un habit rouge. . . .
    C'était ma jup' bordée en p'luche. . . .

(*Lui:*) . . . Quel était donc ce grand homm' noir, . . .
    Dedans mon lit, hier au soir? . . .
(*Elle:*) . . . Ce n'était pas un grand homm' noir. . . .
    C'était votre vieille grand'mère. . . .

(*Lui:*) . . . Est-ce, dis-moi, que les grand'mères, . . .
    Port'nt une grande barbe noire? . . .
(*Elle:*) . . . C'était d'avoir mangé des mûres. . . . (*bis*)

(*Lui:*) . . . Y a-t-il des pays, sur la terre, . . .
    Où ya des mûr's en plein hiver? . . .
(*Elle:*) . . . Dedans le jardin chez mon père, . . .
    Yen a des vert's, yen a des mûres. . . .

(*Lui:*) . . . Va m'en chercher, pour que j'en mange! . . .(*bis*)
(*Elle:*) . . . Nous les avons toutes mangées. . . .
    Avons mangé jusqu'à la branche. . . .

(*Lui:*) . . . Vous êt's une femme rusée. . . . (*bis*)

(*Elle:*) . . . Je ne suis pas   femme rusée. . . .
Je suis votre femme épousée. . . .


(*Lui:*) . . . Mets toi ici,   genoux en terre, . . .
Que je te tranch',   d'un coup, la tête! . . .

(*Elle:*) . . . Que votre volonté soit faite. . . .
J'en aurai la conscience nette! . . .


(*Lui:*) . . . Relève-toi,   je te pardonne! . . .
Les femmes sont   plus fin's que l'homme. . . .

(*Elle:*) . . . Mais bien avant   que soit l'automne, . . .
Je vous ferai   pousser des cornes. . . .


(*Lui:*) . . . Répète donc   ce que tu dis? . . . (*bis*)

(*Elle:*) . . . Mais bien avant   que tu t'endormes, . . .
Je te ferai manger des pommes. . . .


## Corbleu, Marion

(*He:*) *Morbleu, Sambleu, Marion,*
And where were you so late last night? *Sambleu!*
And where were you so late last night? *Corbleu!*

(*She:*) I swear, O husband mine,
That I was by the running water,
I swear I went to wash your woollen stocking, *I swear!*


(*He:*) *Morbleu, Sambleu, Marion,*
I don't believe 't would take so long, *Sambleu!*
I don't believe 't would take so long, *Corbleu!*

(*She:*) I swear, O husband mine,
The running stream was very dirty,
I swear, the running stream was very dirty, *I swear.*


(*He:*) *Morbleu, Sambleu, Marion,*
Who was it fouled the running stream? *Sambleu!* (*bis*)

(*She:*) I swear, O husband mine,
It was the Queen of France's horses, *I swear.* (*bis*)

76

(*He:*) *Morbleu, Sambleu, Marion,*
    And who was he, that gay young spark, *Sambleu!*
    Within my room so late at night? *Corbleu!*
(*She:*) I swear 'twas not a man,
    'Twas not a man within your chamber,
    I swear it was Nannette, your little cousin. *I swear!*

(*He:*) *Morbleu, Sambleu, Marion,*
    I don't believe 't would take so long, *Sambleu!*
    I don't believe 't would take so long, *Corbleu!*
(*She:*) I swear it was Nannette,
    Your little cousin, in my chamber.
    I swear it was Nannette, your little cousin, *I swear!*

(*He:*) *Morbleu! Sambleu! Marion,*
    He had a beard, no girl was he, *Sambleu!*
    He had a beard, no girl was he, *Corbleu!*
(*She:*) I swear her mouth was black
    Because she'd eaten huckleberries,
    I swear her mouth was black from huckleberries, *I swear!*

Among the many songs called *maumariés* or *mal mariés,* none is more sarcastic and witty than this debate between a deceived husband and an unfaithful wife. It was made famous by Yvette Guilbert, to whom it was a standby (*pièce de résistance*). The melody which this Paris singer used was not, however, as interesting as the Canadian version here presented. Canadians and Acadians have preserved this song with all its jongleurian tang, perhaps adding a bit of their own. They were themselves acquainted, it seems, with this type of domestic upheaval.

Peculiarly enough, singers liked to extol conjugal strife rather than wedded bliss, which remains unsung in their repertory. It is said that a happy people remain without a history. Sir Harold Boulton's translation given here is of a single Canadian version submitted to him in 1929, whereas the French form given here was edited in 1946 from a larger number of records, *hence their differences.*

The prosody again is of the folk (jongleur) variety, with four or five syllables for the first hemistich, plus four for the second, eight beats in all. The endings or rhymes are feminine in pairs. Some features enhance the relative antiquity of the composition: in particular the tune, which is Dorian (in D), as in epic chants. The text, too, with its playful mood alternating with deep tones, is truly characteristic of medieval times.

This dialogued song is one of the best known in French collections. It figures in many compilations, among them *Les plus célèbres chansons de France,* edition by Paul Ollendorff, p. 35 (without a tune).[1] In the Canadian repertory—which is Canadian rather than Acadian— the text and melodies surpass in quality and fullness their parallels from the motherland. In particular that of Mme. Ringuet-Panneton, of Three Rivers, is the most complete and nearest to the original. The fine Dorian tune reproduced here is that of Mme. François Michaud, recorded at Saint-André (Kamouraska), in 1918 (No. 1808). The present French text is drawn mostly from the Ringuet-Panneton version.[2]

## REFERENCES AND SOURCES

### Published:

1. Barbeau, *Alouette!,* 136–140 (Bibliog. 59).

2. Père Germain Lemieux, s. j., under the title "Corbleur, sambleur," in *Folklore Franco-Ontarien,* 44–45 (Bibliog. 74).

3. Sœur Marie Ursule, "Corbleur, sambleur, O Marie-Anne," in "Civilisation traditionnelle des Lavalois," 287 (Bibliog. 83).

### Sources:

1–12. Twelve versions are listed in *Alouette!,* collected by the author from 1916 to 1936, in the following locations: Tadoussac, Port-Daniel (Acadian), Gascon (Bonaventure), two versions from La Tourelle (Gaspé), Saint-André (Kamouraska), Portage (Temiscouata), Saint-François (Île d'Orléans); in the collection of Père Godbout, from Sherbrooke (Quebec); in the collection of Adélard Lambert (Berthier-en-haut); in the author's collection, from Mme. Eva Ringuet-Panneton, in a manuscript, Trois-Rivières. Another version was heard, but not recorded, at Saint-Urbain Charlevoix).

13. In the Acadian collection of J. T. Le Blanc in 1940, from John F. Forest, Cape Pelé, N. B., published in *La Voix d'Évangéline,* No. 9159.

14. In the author's and Laura Boulton's collection in 1941, from Léonidas and Mme. Thadée Lavoie, Saint-Hilarion (Charlevoix).

---

[1] Cf. Child, ballad #274.
[2] See the author's *Alouette!,* 136–140 (Bibliog. 59).

15–17. In the Carmen Roy collection, from Léon Collins, La Tourelle (Gaspé), No. 5528; from Georges Castonguay, Ruisseau-à-Rebours (Gaspé), No. 5568c; from Benoit Noël, Rivière Morris (Gaspé), No. 5791.

18, 19. In the collection of Luc Lacourcière, at Archives de Folklore, Quebec, from Mme. Joseph Dufour, île aux Coudres, No. 502; from Mme. Philéas Morneau and Mrs. Armand Bouchard, of Baie-des-Rochers and Saint-Hilarion (Charlevoix) in 1947, No. 293.

20. In the Lacourcière-Savard collection, from Mme. Armand Gagnon and Maurice Duchesne, same district, No. 104.

21. In the Acadian collection of Dr. Dominique Gauthier at Archives de Folklore, from Allard Haché and Vincent V., at Shippigan, N. B., in 1953, No. G142.

# LÉGÈREMENT JE VAIS M'EN ALLER

## QUITE CONTENT AS I GO MY WAY

Chez nous, nous é--tions trois frè---res, tous les _ trois à mari-

er . C'est bien moi qui suis le plus jeune, car je _ vais vous le mon-

. trer. Lé-gèr'ment je vais m'en al-ler, lé-ger'ment je vais m'en al-ler.

## Légèrement je vais m'en aller

Chez nous, nous étions trois frères,   tous les trois à marier.
C'est bien moi qui suis le plus jeune,   car je vais vous le montrer.
    *Légèr'ment je vais m'en aller. (bis)*

Je vais entrer dans la danse,   c'est pour un' ami' chercher.
Je me retourne et me détourne,   je n'en trouv' pas de mon gré.

Mais j'en vois un' de bonne mine;   je vais aller la d'mander.
"Donnez-moi votr' bell' main blanche,   avec moi venez danser!

En vous faisant la révérence   vous plaîrait-il mais de m'aimer?"
"Oh! je vois bien à votr' mine   ce n'est pas moi qu'vous aimez.

Car je vois à votre sourire   que c'est ell' qu' vous désirez.
Oh! donnez-moi votre main blanche;   j'vais aller vous présenter."


## Quite Content as I Go My Way

There are three brothers in our family   all fitted for the married
   state.
And of the three I am the youngest,   as I will now to you relate.

> *Life for me is a journey gay,*
> *Quite content as I go my way.*

I thought I'd take a turn at dancing,   if I could find a lady fair,
I took a look around about me,   but could not find a partner there.

At last a lady caught my fancy;   I went up to her eagerly.
"Your snow-white hand I pray you give me,   and come and dance a
   turn with me.

My best respects I beg to offer,   to be my love could you incline."
"Oh, from your manner I feel certain   the love you want it is not
   mine.

For I perceive the way you're smiling   another lady you prefer.
Your snow-white hand I pray you give me,   and I'll present you now
   to her."


Folk dances in French Canada or New France, which here embraces
Quebec, Acadia, Missouri, and Louisiana, are very many. Most of
them are ancient and traditional, brought over from the provinces of
France in the seventeenth century. But a certain number, especially
the reels, jigs, and square dances with calls, reflect the cultural influence of the Scottish and Irish settlers in the region, who followed
the British conquest of North America.

As a rule they may be classified into:

1. Dances accompanied by songs, some of them *rondes,* like the archaic *Danse du rosier, L'Avoine, La fille du coupeur de paille, La danse du mouchoir, Ramenez vos moutons, bergère, Petite hirondelle,* for girls. Some of these are of the *danses-promenade* type, or open rondes in a file or a ring. Many others belong to a different type, being meant for social games, collective work (with solos and refrains), and lively entertainment for both men and women. For instance: *M'en vas à la fontaine* is a fuller song, *Le lendemain que je m'suis marié,* a drinking song and step dance, *La liptitou, C'était la fille d'un cantinier, Veillez, veillez, Marie Picard.*

2. Dances accompanied by instruments, such as reels, jigs, quadrilles, cotillons, and the now most popular square dances with calls.

*Légèrement je vas m'en aller* belongs to the *danse-promenade* or social-game type, in which both men and women take part, curtseying to one another.

It has been recorded, so far as we know, only in Quebec, from Montreal down the Saint Lawrence to Kamouraska.

# AVEC SON AIGUILLE

## WITH HIS NEEDLE

## Avec son aiguille

M'en r'venant des noc's,   de la rue Saint-Vallier,
Dans mon chemin j'rencontr'   la bonn' fem' Jean Caillé.

*Beti betan delum*
(Parlé:) *kt, kt!*
*Beti betan delum*
*a la dé!*

Dans mon chemin j'rencontr'   la bonn' fem' Jean Caillé.
Elle m'a dit bonjour,   ell' m'a dit de rentrer.

Ell' m'a donné un' chaise:   "Approchez-vous jaser!"
"Ce n'est pas vous, madam',   que je suis v'nu chercher."

83

C'est vot' fill' Moniqu',   savoir si je l'aurai?"
"Je donn'rai pas ma fill'   au méchant couturier.

Car avec son aiguille   il pourrait la piquer."
"Que le diable emport'   l'aiguille et mon métier!"

*N'eus' 'té que* d'mon aiguille,   je me s'rais mari-é
Avec la plus bell' fille   du bonhomm' Jean Caillé,

Avec la plus bell' fille   du bonhomm' Jean Caillé.
Elle a des bell's mains blanches,   des beaux cheveux bouclés.

## With His Needle

From the wedding feast   at Rue Saint Valier,
Coming home I met the wife   of goodman Jean Caillé.

> *Beti betan delum,*
> (Spoken:) *kt, kt!*
> *Beti betan delum*
> *a la dé!*

There I met the wife of goodman Jean Caillé.
"Good day, come in," she said,    "to pass the time o' day."

She offered me a chair,   "Let's have a chat," said she.
"It was not you, Madame, that I came here to see.

'Twas your child Moniqu'   'tis her I come to woo."
"I'll never give my child   to tailors such as you.

For with your needle sharp   you'd prick her, I'm afraid."
"Devil take the needle then,   the needle is my trade."

If t'were not for that,   I should have had my way,
And have wed the lovely child   of goodman Jean Caillé.

I'd have wed the child   of goodman Jean Caillé,
With her hands so snowy white,   and curls in trim array.


Of the same type as *La mariée s'y baigne* (p. 149), but less extensively known and slightly deviating from the theme which hinges
upon the shoemaker, this paddling and dancing song picks up the
tailor (*couturier*) for the target of its fun-making. Instead of a bed
bedecked with roses, it ends up with a curse: "To the devil with my
trade and needle, if it's only good to prick my sweetheart!"

Its refrain, longer than the previous one, adapts it to the needs of
the dance rather than of the paddle in the canoe. And its lines consist
of two halves of six beats each, both of them masculine. And the
whole story is uniformly rhyming in *é*, like epic poems of medieval
times.

We find it in only a few records, one in Acadia, one in Temiscouata
down the Saint Lawrence, one near Quebec, one near Montreal, and
another from New Ontario.

## REFERENCES AND SOURCES

**Published:**

1. Père Anselme and Frère Daniel Boudreau of Chéticamp, Cape
Breton, in *Chansons d'Acadie*, 2nd Series, 30: "Dans mon chemin
j'rencontre un gentil cavalier . . . Wing trala . . ."; National Museum, No. 4365 (Bibliog. 57).

2. Père Germain Lemieux, s. j. in *Folklore Franco-Ontarien*, 10–11:
"M'en allant à la chasse . . . aux perdrix, Laridel: patapet. . . .
(Bibliog. 74).

3. Sœur Marie Ursule, in "Civilisation traditionnelle des Lavalois,"
*Les Archives de Folklore* 5–6:337: "Bonjour, la compagnie, approchez-
vous du feu. . . ." (Bibliog. 83).

**Sources:**

1. Recorded by the author in 1918 from Luc April, Portage (Temiscouata), No. 1601: reproduced here.

2. E. Z. Massicotte in 1919 from Philéas Bédard, Saint-Remi-de-
Napierville, No. 1478: "C'est un p'tit cordonnier Qui veut s'y marier
. . . Latetour lour, lour. . . ."

# AU CABARET

## AT THE CABARET

## Au cabaret

Le lendemain   que j'me suis marié,  
   Ma femme a voulu me battre. } *(bis)*  
Au cabaret   j'me suis en allé  
   Trouver mes amis pour boire,  
     Trouver mes amis *(ter)*  
      Pour boire.

86

"Mes chers amis,   ne buvons pas tant,⎤
   Car je vois venir ma femme.            ⎦ (bis)
Elle est là-bas,   elle est sur ces côtes.
   Je l'entends déjà qui gronde,
      Je l'entends déjà   (ter)
         Qui gronde."


Bien promptement   ell' vient au cabaret:⎤
   "Sors d'ici,   ivrogne du diable!"       ⎦ (bis)
"Du cabaret   ah oui! j'en sortirai,
   Quand j'aurai fini de boire,
      Quand j'aurai fini'   (ter)
         De boire."


"Mon cher mari,   ah! si tu continues,⎤
   Tu feras périr ta famille!            ⎦ (bis)
Un pied chaussé,   et puis, l'autre nu.
   File à la maison, ivrogne!
      File à la maison,   (ter)
         Ivrogne!"


## At the Cabaret

The morning that followed my wedding day,⎤
   My good wife she wanted to beat me.      ⎦ (bis)
I made my way toward the cabaret,
   Where my friends were drinking, drinking,
   Everyone was drinking,
   Everyone was drinking,
   Everyone was drinking, drinking.


"Friends, let me warn you not to drink so much,⎤
   For I see my wife a-coming.                   ⎦ (bis)
Look where she comes, I see her in the offing.
   Can't you hear her scolding, scolding? . . ."

Quickly she found us in the cabaret. ⎱ (bis)
  "Get you out of here, you drunkard!" ⎰
"I won't delay to leave the cabaret,
  When I've finished drinking, drinking. . . ."

"Husband of mine, if you continue so, ⎫ (bis)
  You'll destroy your loving fam'ly! ⎭
One shoe is on, the other shoe is missing.
  Get you to your home, you drunkard! . . ."

This staccato song is meant for the dance, but it also has the flavor of a drinking song. Its theme is familiar in folk literature. Here again are the *maumariés* squabbling with each other. The husband, a toper, wastes his estate and distresses his friends while "rolling the bottle" at the inn. For this his wife reproaches him, in another version of the song which differs from the above:

> Mon mari boit plus qu'un glouton,
> Cent fois plus qu'il n'a de rente.
> Son habit n'a plus de bouton.
> Mais son nez en a bien trente.

But the inveterate drinker is far from submitting meekly to the scolding wife when she storms upon him, growling. He retorts, in the same vein:

> Ne fais pas tant la mégère!
> Manche à balais, t'en auras.

That is, if you keep on, you shall taste of the broomstick.

The wife must submit to her fate. She who tried to thrash him the day after the wedding now can only yell at him: "Get out, you the devil's pal!" And the next day she drives him back home brandishing a green sapling over his head. "Back home!" she cries, or, "If you persist, your family is doomed!"

This song may have survived only in Canada and Acadia; apparently it has not in France or in Louisiana, in spite of the inn (*cabaret*) not being a feature of rural life in the New World.[1] The twelve ver-

---

[1] Two stanzas in a different song of the same type are quoted by Champfleury and Wekerlin, in *Chansons populaires des provinces de France,* for Saintonge, 76:
> Allons, ivrogne,
> Retourn' voir à ton logis, (*bis*)
> Tes enfants sur la paille,
> Tu manges tout ton bien, Tirelin, Avecque des canailles.

sions so far recorded in French Canada come from widely scattered centers: [2] E. Z. Massicotte and Adélard Lambert found it on the upper and middle Saint Lawrence River, at Beauharnois, Valleyfield, and Berthier-en-haut. Sœur Marie Ursule discovered it at Laval next to Quebec City. The text and tune reproduced here are from François Saint-Laurent, at La Tourelle, Gaspé. Carmen Roy has taken it down thrice at other points in Gaspé. It was also heard at Port-Daniel, Chaleur Bay. And the Rev. Mr. Arsenault received it from his old mother on Prince Edward Island, in the very midst of Acadia, in the Gulf of Saint Lawrence.

Arranged for four male voices, it was performed at the Second Quebec Festival at Château Frontenac in 1928 and was published along with others in Boston, Massachusetts under the title of *French-Canadian Folk-Songs . . . for Chorus and Men's Voices,* by Sir Ernest MacMillan (Boston Music Co., G. Schirmer). And Sir Ernest was awarded the Beatty prize.

The words of the song are disposed into a mixed pattern, the stanzas consisting of six lines with final syllables intercrossing, some of them masculine, the others, feminine; and the rhymes, if ever there were any, have been lost. The lines are of unequal length: ten, eight, five, two. The lilting tune is 2/4 and 1/4, in C major with the tonic on D.

## REFERENCES AND SOURCES

**Published:**

1–7. Seven versions were recorded by the author from 1918 to 1923 and were published in *Romancero du Canada,* 243–245. Three of these, in the Massicotte collection at the National Museum, 1918–1927, are from Valleyfield, Saint-Timothée (Beauharnois), and from the Quebec district. One was recorded by Adélard Lambert in 1925, which is quite different from the others. Three were collected by the author, two in La Tourelle (Gaspé) in 1918, and an Acadian version at Port-Daniel in 1923 (Bibliog. 44).

8. Père Anselme and Frère Daniel Boudreau, of Cheticamp, Cape Breton, in 1942, in *Chansons d'Acadie,* 3rd Series, 31: "C'est aujourd'hui j'me suis marié. . . ." (Bibliog. 69).

9. Sœur Marie Ursule, "Civilisation traditionnelle des Lavalois," in *Les Archives de Folklore* 5–6:315: "Je demande à ma femme" (Bibliog. 83).

---

[2] Barbeau, *Romancero du Canada,* 245 (Bibliog. 44).

**Sources:**

1–3. Recorded by Carmen Roy at La Tourelle (Gaspé) from L. Collins, *ca.* 1950, No. 5156; from Benoit Noël, Rivière Morris near Rivière-au-Renards, No. 5409; and from Napoléon Poirier in 1951 at Saint-Siméon (Gaspé): "Amis, buvons divertissons-nous!"

Add

# À LA CLAIRE FONTAINE

## *BY THE CLEAR FOUNTAIN*

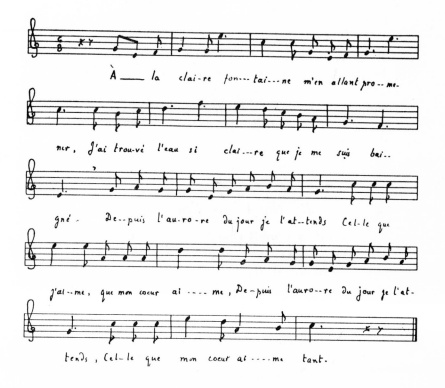

À ___ la clai-re fon---tai---ne m'en allant pro--me-

ner, J'ai trou-vé l'eau si clai---re que je me suis bai--

gné . De--puis l'au-ro-re Du jour je l'at--tends Cel-le que

j'ai--me, que mon coeur ai ---- me, De--puis l'auro--re Du jour je l'at-

tends , Cel-le que mon coeur ai ---- me tant.

## À la claire fontaine

À la claire fontaine   m'en allant promener,
J'ai trouvé l'eau si claire   que je m'y suis baigné.

*Depuis l'aurore du jour je l'attends,*
*Celle que j'aime, que mon cœur aime.*
*Depuis l'aurore du jour je l'attends,*
*Celle que mon cœur aime tant.*

C'est au pied d'un grand chêne,   je me suis fait sécher.
Sur la plus haute branche   le rossignol chantait.

Chante, rossignol, chante,   toi qui as le cœur gai!
Tu as le cœur à rire,   moi je l'ai à pleurer.

J'ai perdu ma maîtresse   sans l'avoir mérité,
Pour un bouquet de roses   que je lui refusai.

Je voudrais que la rose   fût encore au rosier.
Et que le rosier même   fût à la mer jeté.

Et que le rosier même   fût à la mer jeté.
Je voudrais que la belle   fût encore à m'aimer.


## By the Clear Fountain

Hard by a lovely clear fountain,
One day I chanced to go.
So fresh and cool the water
That I must plunge below.

*Rising at dawn I am wearying for*
*One whom my heart must love evermore.*
*Rising at dawn I am wearying for*
*One whom alone I can adore.*

Then as I waited to dry me
Under a tall elm tree,
A nightingale was singing
His lovely song to me.

Sing nightingale so sweetly!
Sing me the song that cheers.
Yours is the heart for laughter,
Mine is the heart for tears.

Now have I lost my dear lady,
Though undeserved my lot,
All for a bunch of roses,
Roses I gave her not.

Would that the festal rose-flower
Still on the bush might be,
And I could cast the rosebush
Into the deep, deep sea!

I would be casting that rosebush
Into the deep, deep sea,
If but my dearest lady
Could be again with me.

Of all the folksongs in old and New France, this is one of the two or three best known and most famous. It is also a masterpiece of oral literature and melody. For French Canada it has been used as a national anthem. It came to the shores of the New World with the seventeenth-century colonists, and has followed them wherever they went, in their labors and adventures. Its lilting rhythm—it is sung to various tunes—has helped them in building their dwellings, pushing back the forests, breaking up the sod, and performing various tasks in barn, shed, shop, and house.

When leaving on a voyage, launching a canoe, mounting a horse or entering a *calèche* (cab), they would at once intone *À la claire fontaine* or *Trois beaux canards* or *À Saint-Malo* (see below), the three foremost favorites.

These familiar tunes served as passports, symbols, and national flags. They peopled the wild solitudes, conjured up the past, and brought together robust arms in a common effort. They may be said to have discovered the New World, for they first awakened the wilderness to the coming of the white man.

Of the three songs mentioned, *À la claire fontaine* is the loveliest, also the most nostalgic. The masterpiece of a fifteenth- or sixteenth-century jongleur of central France (in *langue d'oïl*), its *distiques* (stanzas in twin lines) consist of lines of twelve syllables with epic cæsura (6f + 6). And they follow the prosodic pattern according to which the cæsuras are all epic or feminine and the endings are masculine uniformly in *-é*. So they form altogether a single epic lay (*laisse épique*).

Its tune, at first and last in C major (Bb in this setting), momentarily engages, seemingly, into the mode of E, in a long refrain which accompanied manual labor. The less familiar of two different melodies, i.e., the one given here, is also used in France. This identity of tune, after centuries of separation, is rather obscure. The air varies far more readily than the words, for each singer is apt to yield to his own mannerisms in singing.

*À la claire fontaine* has been published countless times in Canada. In the limited list of publications below, twelve different quotations have been selected, of as many versions. Thirty-five versions are listed for all parts of Acadia and Canada, but not Louisiana.

## REFERENCES AND SOURCES

**Published:**

1. LaRue, in *Le Foyer canadien* (Bibliog. 1).
2. In *Petit Chansonnier comique,* 1861: "M'en r'venant des noces . . . bien fatigué. . . . Ah! je l'attends."
3. Ernest Gagnon, *Chansons populaires du Canada* (Bibliog. 2).
4. William McLennan, *French Songs of Old Canada,* 2–7 (Bibliog. 5).
5. William Parker Greenough, *Canadian Folk-Life and Folk-Lore,* 133, 134 (Bibliog. 4).
6. Julien Tiersot, *Songs of the People,* 6–13 (Bibliog. 7).
7. Barbeau, *Folk-Songs of Old Quebec,* 40, 41 (Bibliog. 40).
8. ———, *Aux armes, Canadiens!,* 5 (Bibliog. 49).
9. Père Anselme and Frère Daniel Boudreau, *Chansons d'Acadie,* 2ème série, 1945, 19 (Bibliog. 57).
10. François Brassard, in *Les Archives de Folklore* 1:42 (Bibliog. 62).
11. Père Germain Lemieux, *Folklore Franco-Ontarien,* 34 (Bibliog. 74).
12. ———, 1950, 10, 11, 13. Also see Sœur Marie Ursule, "Civilisation traditionnelle des Lavalois," *Les Archives de Folklore* 5–6:360, 434 (Bibliog. 83).

94

**Sources:**

1. A manuscript entitled "Annales musicales du Petit-Cap," of the Archives du Séminaire de Quebec, bearing the names of Hamel and Doherty, two priests of the institution *ca.* 1860, contains five airs of this song.

2. Acadian version recorded *ca.* 1924 by the Rev. P. Arsenault of Mont Carmel, Prince Edward Island.

3. Collected by the author from Adélard Lambert, *ca.* 1930, from Berthier-en-haut, No. 3261.

4. Author, from Frère Onésime Ménard, O.M.I., Sainte-Justine, Vaudreuil, in 1953; published in *La Patrie,* July 5, 1953, p. 21.

5. Author, from Mme. Adéline Landry, eighty-six years old, of Havre Aubert, Îles Madeleine, living in Montreal, 1948.

6. Author, from Henri Lefebvre, Ottawa, who learned it from Maria Olivier Lefebvre, at Laprairie, and called it *chanson à repondre.*

7. Collected by E. Z. Massicotte, as sung by V. F. de Repentigny, in 1917, and learned at Saint-Timothée (Beauharnois), No. 1218.

8. Collected by Massicotte from the manuscript songbook of Mizaël Hamelin of Saint-Roch-de-Quebec.

9. Massicotte, 1917: "J'ai trouve l'eau si belle . . . oui, je l'attends, mon amant, ce printemps."

10. Massicotte, another version: "Oui, je l'attends, mon amant, Patati pataton. . . ."

11–19. Collected by J. T. Le Blanc in his Acadian collection and published in *La Voix d' Évangéline,* Moncton, *ca.* 1937; a version from Mme. Malvina Landry, Pointe-Rocheuse, near Caraquet, N. B., No. 9577; from Mme. Elise Girouard, Kent Boom, N. B., No. 9578; from Mme. Joseph Léger, Moncton, No. 9579; from Mlle. Georgina Mazerolle, Village Saint Jean, N. B., No. 9580; from Tilmon T. Le Blanc, Bronson Sett, N. B., No. 9581; from Mme. David Le Blanc, Hartford, Conn., No. 9582; from Hélène Daigle, Acadieville, N. B., No. 9584; from Mme. Joseph Bordage, Saint Luc, Kent Co., N. B., No. 9585; from Mme. André Arsenault, Saint Chrisostome, Prince Edward Island, No. 9586.

20, 21. Collected by François Brassard, two versions published in *20ᵉ Siècle,* Ottawa, June 1944, p. 194, from Nos. 15 and 214 in his collection, presumably from the neighborhood of Chicoutimi.

22–26. From the same collection, and obtained from Orphila Mathieu, North Bay, Ont., 1947, No. 292; from David Brossard, Saint-Jérome, Lac Saint-Jean, 1941; from Urbain Petit, Strickland, Ont.,

1943; published in *l'Alma Mater*, Chicoutimi, Dec. 1941, p. 51; from Mme. Pierre Bélanger, 1941.

27. Collected by Brother Marcellin-André, from Rosario Groulx, at Sainte-Thérèse-de-Blainville (Terrebonne) in 1946.

28. Collected by Marcel Rioux, from Joseph Fraser, Île-Verte (Rivière-du-Loup) in 1948.

29–34. Collected by Luc Lacourcière and the Rev. Félix Antoine Savard, for the Archives de Folklore from Jean-Baptiste Ferron, Île Shippigan, N. B., 1951, No. 1155; from Onias Ferron, same locality, in 1952, No. 1232; from Mme. Alexandre Gauvin, 1950, Pidgeon Hill, Île Shippigan, No. 945; from Pierre Haché, 1950, at Saint-Raphael-sur-Mer, Île Shippigan, No. 938; from Alphonse Doyon, Scott (Beauce), in 1948, No. 630; from Joseph Joncas, Percé (Gaspé), in 1947, No. 411.

35. Collected by Conrad Laforte, from Lorenzo Bouliane, 1955, at Petit-Saguenay (Chicoutimi) No. L247, L16.

36. Collected by Carmen Roy, after 1950; sung as a *ronde* by three schoolgirls at Paspébiac (Bonaventure) No. 6761.

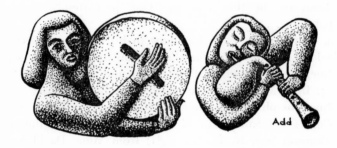

# EN ROULANT MA BOULE

## ROLL MY BALL

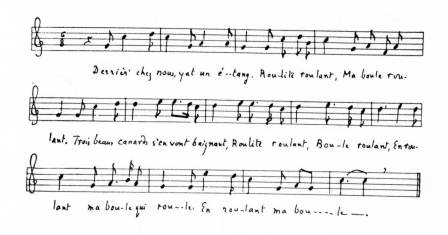

Derrièr' chez nous, yat un é--tang. Roulite roulant, Ma boule rou-

lant. Trois beaux canards s'en vont baignant, Roulite roulant, Bou-le roulant, En rou-

lant ma bou-le qui rou--le, En roulant ma bou----le.—.

## En roulant ma boule

Derrièr' chez nous   yat un étang,

> *Roulite roulant,*
> *Ma boule roulant.*

Trois beaux canards   s'en vont baignant.

> *Roulite roulant,*
> *Boule roulant.*
> *En roulant ma boule qui roule,*
> *En roulant ma boule.*

97

Le fils du roi   s'en va chassant
Avec son grand   fusil d'argent.

Visa le noir,   tua le blanc.
"O fils du roi,   tu es méchant.

Tu as tué   mon canard blanc.
Par ses deux yeux   sort'nt les diamants,

Et par son bec   l'or et l'argent,
Et par sous l'aile   il perd son sang.

Et tout's ses plumes   s'en vont au vent.
Y sont trois dames   les ramassant.

Et nous ferons   un lit de camp.
Nous coucherons   tous deux dedans.

Pour y avoir   des p'tits enfants . . .
Nous en aurons   des p'tits, des grands."


## Roll My Ball

Behind our home and out beyond,

*Then merrily roll my ball around.*

Three ducks are swimming on a pond.

*Then merrily roll, merrily roll,*
*Roll my ball, my ball around,*
*And roll my ball, my ball around.*

A-hunting came the king's own son,
A-hunting with his silver gun.

He saw the black, he killed the white.
"O naughty prince, that wasn't right!

How wrong my lovely duck to kill.
Two diamond drops his eyes distill.

His beak with gold and silver glows.
Beneath his wing the red blood flows.

His feathers float upon the breeze,
Three maidens catch them 'neath the trees.

A marriage bed they will provide
Where we may slumber side by side.

And there we'll raise a fam'ly fine,
Both big and little, lover mine."

This song and the next comprise two of the ninety-two variants of the famous French-Canadian paddle song presented by the author under the title *Trois beaux canards*.[1]

But so characteristically Canadian is *En roulant ma boule* in some ways that we are apt to forget that it is an old-country possession as well. Our list of versions, though still incomplete, includes at least twenty-nine versions from France and a large number from Canada; and parallels have been published by C. Nigra for northern Italy.[2]

While the refrain *Rouli, roulant, ma boule roulant, en roulant ma boule* is the only one extensively known in Canada, many other forms were also found in both old and New France. A number of these are still remembered by the older folk singers, such as: *Levez les pieds gaillardement!*, or *Gaillardement, je suis brune, gaillarde brune, je suis brune gaillardement,* or again *V'là l'bon vent, v'là l'joli vent, v'là l'bon vent, m'amie m'attend.*

To test the extent of the diffusion of this one of the most popular French songs in North America, the author made and published in

---

[1] See Bibliog. 68.
[2] In *Les Archives de Folklore* 2:97–138 (1947).

1947 a searching study of *Trois beaux canards* [3] and found that 92 Canadian versions were then available. And, as may be seen in the appended list, fifteen more versions have been recorded, bringing the total up to at least 107.

The significant outcome of the survey of this one song going back to the fifteenth century is that there is a common text for all the variants, consisting of fifteen lines aligned into a single epic lay, all the lines rhyming in -*an,* and each line is cut in two halves with masculine endings. But there ends its uniformity. No less than thirty or forty different songs—with distinct tunes and refrains—have been made from it, in the course of time, to respond to the need for new materials. A part of this ramification of an original composition took place in the motherland before the migration of colonists to the New World in the seventeenth century, but a wider development has occurred since and is reflected mostly in the lilting tunes and the contents of the refrains or choruses, such as: *Tout le long de la rivière, Le vent du nord m'appelle, Canot d'écorce qu'il vole, C'est l'aviron qui nous monte, Nous ramerons tous, Je veux voyager, Je pique et je drave, Vive la compagnie!*

The version given here was recorded in 1916 from Edouard Hovington, an old canoeman of Tadoussac, Quebec. He was then nearly ninety years old. As it differs slightly from the current printed records and was learned before songbooks were in circulation, we presume that it is an authentic and uncontaminated version.

Popularity [4] and print, even more than desuetude, tend to rob a folksong of some of its most engaging features. They flatten it down to a level of mediocrity; and in Canada they have reduced to the commonplace such pretty work songs as *Roll My Ball* and *At Saint-Malo.*

---

[3] T. F. Crane, in his *Chansons populaires de la France,* 270, gives several references to which we add others: E. Rolland, *Recueil de chansons populaires,* vol. 1, 249–254; vol. 2, 147—six versions from Lorient and Retonféy; de Puymaigre, *Chants populaires recueillis dans le pays messin,* 396; de Beaurepaire, *Étude sur la poésie populaire en Normandie,* lxxxviii; C. Guillon, *Chansons populaires de l'Ain,* 542; J. F. Bladé, *Poésies populaires de la Gascogne,* vol. 3, 212; *Mélusine* 1, col. 459 (Lorient); A. Orain, *Les canards blancs,* 101–103; J. Bujeaud, *Chants et chansons populaires des provinces de l'ouest,* vol. 1, 134, 135; Jean Huré, *Chansons et danses bretonnes,* 15; L. Lambert, *Chants et chansons populaires du Languedoc,* vol. 1, 349, 350—two variants; A. Millien, *Chants et chansons populaires du Nivernais,* vol. 2, 22–29, with eleven different melodies and refrains; M. Stoober, *Elsassisches Volksbuchlein,* 162. For Italian versions, see C. Nigra, *Canti popolari del Piemonte,* 334. In Canada it was published in the fifties in *Recueil de chansons canadiennes et françaises,* 67, 68; in LaRue, *Le Foyer canadien* 1:340, who also cites a French version by J. J. Ampère; in E. Gagnon, *Chansons populaires du Canada,* and elsewhere.

[4] See Barbeau and Sapir, *Folk Songs of French Canada,* 116–120 (Bibliog. 14).

100

Familiar at first among canoemen, these ditties have for more than a generation passed into the small repertory of every household, school, and shop. They were among the earliest to be published, back in the 1850s, and have since obstinately occupied the forefront—the shop-window, we might say—of every Canadian songbook, large or small. They have taken on a significance somewhat analogous to that of the maple leaf or the beaver on our national flags. But what they gained on the surface they lost in depth. At one time they had many variants in tune and text. They shared in the inimitable musical quality of the best folk melodies, unspoiled by the sluggish throats of the "educated" class. But it is almost too late to find them in uncontaminated form even in their former haunts. A blighting uniformity has come over them.

Yet *Roll My Ball* is a graceful, witty song, whose imagery is enlivened with a playful turn in the last stanzas. Its melody is bright and rollicking, though restricted in scope and color. Many an echo in the wilds of America has been awakened by the coming of the first white man with his fanciful evocation of its "three white-feather ducks a-bathing," and "the son of the king" with his "gun of silver, silver-bright," taking aim at the black and killing the white! For three centuries it has accompanied, as a paddling song with alternating solo and chorus, the pioneer canoemen, *coureurs de bois,* and explorers up and down the rivers and across the prairie, the wasteland, and the mountain. And now it looks as though it has come to the end of its course, like the birchbark canoe and the travois. The virgin forest and river, once its congenial background, have been defaced by ubiquitous lumber camps, drifting logs, dikes, sawmills, and forest fires.

## REFERENCES AND SOURCES

**Published:**

1. Julien Tiersot, *Songs of the People* (Bibliog. 7).
2. Barbeau, *Veillées du bon vieux temps,* 19 (Bibliog. 9).
3. "A-Rolling my Ball," in *Folk Songs of French Canada,* Barbeau and Sapir, 117–120 (Bibliog. 14).
4. Barbeau, *Romancero,* 151, 154 (Bibliog. 44).
5. ———, *Come A Singing!,* 56, 57 (Bibliog. 66).
6. ———, *Aux armes, Canadiens!,* 4 (Bibliog. 49).
7. ———, "V'là l'bon vent," in *Alouette!,* 38–40 (Bibliog. 59).
8. An exhaustive study by the author of ninety-two versions of this work song may be consulted in *Les Archives de Folklore* 2:97–138 (Bibliog. 68).

9. Corinne L. Saucier, *Histoire et traditions de la paroisse des Avoyelles en Louisiane*, 421, 422 (Bibliog. 73).

10. Père Germain Lemieux, *Folklore Franco-Ontarien* (Bibliog. 74).

**Sources:**

Additional versions recorded since 1945 or overlooked on a previous date:

In a manuscript in the Archives du Séminaire de Quebec, *ca.* 1860, under the title of "Archives musicales du Petit-Cap," by Hamel and Doherty, with five tunes.

99. Collected by Père Archange Godbout in 1918 in Lotbinière or Portneuf county.

100–102. Collected by François Brassard and published in *l'Alma Mater*, Nov. 1949, Chicoutimi, p. 35; in *l'Alma Mater*, Nov. 1950, p. 361; and from Pierre Bélanger, Chicoutimi: "Derrière chez-nous. . . ."

103. Collected by Gaston Eugène Adam in Louisiana, *ca.* 1944 (Bibliog. 100).

104. Collected by Frère Marcellin André in 1946 from Rosario Groulx, Sainte-Thérèse-de-Blainville (Terrebonne).

105. Collected by the author from Pierrette Cousineau, who recorded it at Saint-Remi-de-Napierville in 1947.

106. From Carmen Roy with informant Albert Lavoie, of Miguasha (Gaspé) in 1950, No. 3747.

107. From Carmen Roy, collected from Angélique Parisé, Paspébiac (Chaleur Bay) No. 5311.

# V'LÀ L'BON VENT!

## WIND SO GAY

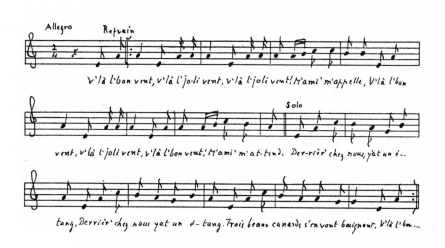

## V'là l'bon vent!

*V'là l'bon vent, v'là l'joli vent,*
*V'là l'bon vent!*
*M'ami' m'appelle.*
*V'là l'bon vent, v'là l'joli vent,*
*V'là l'bon vent!*
*M'ami' m'attend.*

Derrièr' chez nous,    yat un étang. (*bis*)
Trois beaux canards    s'en vont baignant.

103

*V'là l'bon vent . . .*

Trois beaux canards   s'en vont baignant. *(bis)*
Le fils du roi   s'en va chassant, . . .

Avec son grand   fusil d'argent. *(bis)*
Visa le noir,   tua le blanc.

"O fils du roi,   tu es méchant! *(bis)*
Tu as tué   mon canard blanc.

Par ses deux yeux   sort'nt les diamants, *(bis)*
Et par son bec   l'or et l'argent,

Et tout's ses plum's   s'en vont au vent. *(bis)*
Y sont trois dam's   les ramassant.

Et nous ferons   un lit de camp. . . ." *(bis)*

*(The rest of the text is identical with that on p. 97.)*


## Wind So Gay

*Wind so gay, I'm on my way.*
*Tell my sweetheart I am coming.*
*Wind so gay, I'm on my way.*
*Blow me where she awaits to-day!*

Behind our home and out beyond, *(bis)*
Three ducks are swimming on a pond.

*(The rest of the text is identical with that on p. 98.)*


This typical voyageur song is one of the series of ninety-two variants published under the same title in *Les Archives de Folklore* (see Bibliog. 68). More than thirty of these variants have different refrains

which mark and prolong the rhythm of the action in paddling, dancing, or working. The tunes, in Canada, as in France, are varied and
numerous. *Trois beaux canards* is truly popular on two continents.

Its origin, presumably in northern France, is not very ancient. Its
two coupled features of *fils du roi* and *fusil d'argent* indicate the
period  to which it belongs, that is, after the fifteenth century. It was
the composition of a jongleur or folk minstrel whose oral art went
back to the inception of the spoken language and ended with the ap-
pearance of broadsheets—printing gradually substituting itself for
living memory. The good preservation of the text of this song ranks
it among the dated pieces in our repertory, like *Le Prince d'Orange*
and *Le Roi Eugène,* both of which belong to the early sixteenth century.

But *Trois beaux canards* seems a bit older. Its deterioration is more
pronounced and the cluster of its adaptations and tunes around the
main theme indicates the passing of a longer period of gestation. The
variants resemble the growth of a tree. For its evolution, time, space,
and changing backgrounds were needed. A part of its variants or
branches already existed in France at the time when, nearly three hundred years ago, the colonists of Normandy and the Western Provinces
of the Loire River brought them to the New World. On both sides of
the ocean we find similar tunes and refrains. They must have originated before the splitting of the main body at the basis. But from that
moment, Canada contributed its own abundant proliferation in the
late development of tunes and burdens which are its own.

In 1809–1811, Bradbury noted [1] that it was a favorite story of the
Canadian voyageur. And never since has it ceased to stand to the fore
of the canoe songs. We find it in varied and unforeseen places in the
repertory. For instance, the old (in 1916) folk singer Edouard Hovington, a former canoeman of the Hudson's Bay Company, said: "Les
Messieurs, in the early days of Tadoussac, about 1850, used to clamour
for it every minute."

After 1860 LaRue and Gagnon [2] collected several forms of it in the
neighborhood of Quebec, and they were not the first to record them in
writing there. Printed songbooks broadened the circulation of this
song at an early date, at once stamping the mark of uniformity on its

---

[1] John Bradbury, *Travels in the Interior of America . . . including Upper Louisiana . . . Ohio, Kentucky, Territories. . . .* vol. 1, London, 1817, 12, 13.

[2] F. A. H. LaRue, "Les chansons populaires et historiques du Canada," *Le Foyer
canadien,* 1:320–384, and Ernest Gagnon, *Chansons populaires du Canada* (Bibliog.
1 and 2).

face. This effect of printing did not, however, stop the oral flow of its variations among rustic folk elsewhere.

Ninety-two versions figure in the study by the author as mentioned above; and more than a score of other versions have been added since to this impressive total.

Nowhere have we found *Trois beaux canards* in a purely narrative form, that is, without a refrain or burden. Its lines of eight beats (*pieds*), cut in halves at the fourth, end with a masculine assonance, *-an*, as in an epic lay (*laisse épique*). Its hard and sonorous accents, at the cæsura and ending, just like its lilting rhythm, placed it at the service of the canoemen who traveled up and down the wild rivers and forested portages. If all its tunes coupled the lines in each stanza, together with double refrains—interior and final—these distichs are more or less artificial, imposed as they are by the tunes. The last line in the distich, in changing the melodic phrase, becomes the first of the next stanza, thus riding on both and prolonging at pleasure the duration of the song. And this lengthening process enhances its usefulness to manual workers.

The function of the song is made obvious by the shape of its tunes and the elaboration of its burdens. To avoid the monotony of repetition while at work or dancing, more and more refrains were in demand, and, whenever inspiration prompted, new tunes and syllables were added to the already large repertory. So long with the main theme came from France the following burdens: *En roulant ma boule; Mon gentil cœur vole au vent; Le vent vire, le vire vent; O ma mie, je vous aime tant; Non, je n'aime pas ces amants volages; Je suis brune gaillardement; Sur le vert, joli vert, joli vert, J'entends le renard, le lièvre, Je suis noire gaillardement.*

Once off the coasts of France, the singers sailed free on the wing of invention, composing more tunes and refrains as they proceeded abroad or traveled into the New World. Of this type, which we may consider Canadian, we count at least twenty in our repertory. They derive their pattern from French prototypes, yet they are somewhat different—for instance: *Lève ton pied légèrement; Bergère, ah! gai lon là!; V'là l'bon vent; Entrez, beau berger!; Vous m'aimerez toujours; Descendez à l'ombre;* etc.

The voyageurs and canoemen soon took hold of this familiar theme and coined many novel airs and burdens, giving them their own lilting stamp, as in *Canot d'écorce qui vole au vent; C'est l'aviron qui nous mène; Nous ramerons tous; Je monte en haut; Je r'descends, je pique, je drave, pis je r'descends sur l'bois carré,* etc.

Taken as a whole, the New World variations of *Trois beaux canards* tend to reverse its Old World equilibrium. They shed its village frippery and don the cruder attire of river, shore, and forest. They stop just short of using moccasins and leggings in the Indian style, of wearing the mackinac jacket, and putting on the red and blue toque and the colorful Assumption sash. Heading into the west wind, the freshly revamped song took hold of the paddle (*aviron*) and beat the running waters up or down stream.

Patrice Coirault, our venerable elder from France, has recently studied its fairly numerous French versions under the name of *Le canard blanc tué par le fils du roi*. He calls it *Chanson à danse, avec le refrain*.[3]

### REFERENCES AND SOURCES

1. Ernest Gagnon, *Chansons populaires du Canada,* 21: "V'là l'bon vent" (Bibliog. 2).

2. P. E. Prévost, *Chansons canadiennes. Paroles et musique par un Canadien* 39 (Bibliog. 6).

3. Barbeau, "*Trois beaux canards* (92 versions canadiennes)" (Bibliog. 68).

---

[3] "Recherches sur notre ancienne chanson populaire traditionnelle," *Bulletin de l'Institut Général psychologique*, Nos. 4–6, 47–66 (1927).

JB

# LES ROSES BLANCHES

## *THE WHITE ROSES*

Par un ma---tin, je me suis le-vé , Par un ma---
tin, je me suis le---vé , ——— Plus ma---tin que ma
tan--te, Là! Plus ma---tin que ma — tan...te.

## Les Roses blanches

Par un matin,   je me suis levé, (*bis*)
Plus matin que ma tante. *Là!* (*bis*)

Dans mon jardin   je m'en suis allé (*bis*)
Cueillir la rose blanche. (*bis*)

Je n'en eus pas   sitôt cueilli trois (*bis*)
Que mon amant y rentre. (*bis*)

"M'ami', faites-moi un bouquet (*bis*)
Qu'il soit de roses blanches!" (*bis*)

La belle en faisant ce bouquet, *(bis)*
Ell' s'est cassé la jambe. *(bis)*

Faut aller q'ri'   le bon médecin *(bis)*
Le médecin de Nantes. *(bis)*

"Bon médecin,   joli médecin, *(bis)*
Que dis-tu de ma jambe?" *(bis)*

"Ta jambe, ma bell',   ne guérira pas, *(bis)*
Qu'ell' n'soit dans l'eau baignante. *(bis)*

Dans un bassin   tout d'or et d'argent, *(bis)*
Couvert de roses blanches." *(bis)*

## *The White Roses*

Early at sunrise, I leave my bed, *(bis)*
While Auntie still reposes, O,
While Auntie still reposes.

Then in the garden I walk alone, *(bis)*
And pick the fresh white roses. *(bis)*

Scarce have I gathered but roses three, *(bis)*
Then here appears my lover. *(bis)*

"Pluck me a bouquet, O love o' mine, *(bis)*
A bouquet of white roses." *(bis)*

As they were culling the lovely flowers, *(bis)*
She fell and broke her ankle. *(bis)*

They had to send for the doctor now. *(bis)*
They had to send to Nantes. *(bis)*

"Doctor, O doctor, come quickly here. *(bis)*
What can you do to heal me?" *(bis)*

"I cannot heal such a break, my child, (*bis*)
It must be bathed in water. (*bis*)

Silver and gold must the basin be, (*bis*)
And heaped with fresh white roses." (*bis*)


*Les Roses blanches,* in the repertory of voyageurs and canoemen, soon drew the attention of English-speaking chroniclers. Ballantyne, in his book on *Hudson Bay* (1843), stated that it was often heard in the subarctic regions. But it has since escaped the attention of our forerunners, LaRue and Gagnon. A canoe song, it has visited—we should say, discovered—the rivers east and west which served the fur trade. It was a symbol of the growing invasion of the wilderness by the white man.

Several explorers and visitors of former days—Talbot, Moore, de la Rochefoucault, de Maufras, and others—have praised in their chronicles the remarkable songs of their Canadian canoemen. For instance, de la Rochefoucault has written:

> Dans toutes les navigations dont sont chargés les Canadiens, les chants commencent dès qu'ils prennent la rame et ne finissent que quand ils la quittent. On se croit dans les provinces de France. Cette illusion fait plaisir. . . ."

Thomas Moore, the Irish poet, who journeyed down the Saint Lawrence in 1803, relates:

> Our Voyageurs had good voices, and sang perfectly in tune together. . . . The original words . . . appeared to be a long incoherent story:

> > Dans mon chemin j'ai rencontré
> > Deux cavaliers très bien montés. . . .

and the Refrain to every verse was:

> > A l'ombre d'un bois je m'en vais jouer;
> > A l'ombre d'un bois, je m'en vais danser.

I ventured to harmonize this air and have published it. Without the charm which association gives to every little memorial of scenes or feelings that are past, the melody may, perhaps, be thought common and trifling; but I remember when we have entered, at sunset, upon one of those beautiful lakes into which the Saint Lawrence so grandly and unexpectedly opens, I have heard this simple air with a pleasure which the finest compositions of the first masters have never given me; and now there is not a note of it which does not recall to my memory the dip of our oars in the Saint Lawrence, the flight of our boat down the Rapids, and all those new and fanciful impressions to which my heart was alive during the whole of this very interesting voyage. . . .

In spite of its vogue, *Les Roses blanches* failed to enter the printed records of the times. It cannot be found in the "Ermatinger Collection of Voyageur Songs" (*ca.* 1830),[1] in *Le Chansonnier canadien* of 1830, or in the *Chansonnier des Collèges* (*ca.* 1840).

Captain George Back, in 1823, was the first who began to collect voyageur songs among canoemen in the service of the Hudson's Bay Company in the course of an expedition to the polar regions on the Coppermine River. And he published a few of them, tunes and translations, in adulterated form. His is the oldest known record of French folksongs, in the New World.[2]

Hubert LaRue of Quebec was the first Canadian who gathered *chansons de terroir* as it was being done in France at the time. He published a dozen, without the airs, in *Le Foyer canadien* in 1863, under the title of "Les Chansons populaires et historiques du Canada." Ernest Gagnon, a young Quebec musician who went over to Paris to study music, came back with the impulse also to collect the songs of his native land, and in 1865 he published his *Chansons populaires du Canada,* a book containing about 100 songs from the neighborhood of Quebec.

After these early efforts, particularly Gagnon's, the harvest should have developed on a large scale. Folk traditions were then in full bloom. Yet the century lapsed without any other exploit in this rich domain. The false impression then developed that the field had been drained; and the rash conclusion soon came to prevail that the whole repertory had been recorded.

In 1914 the recording of Canadian folklore entered a new phase, after the author had discovered that folktales and folksongs could still be harvested by the hundreds. And then the work and collections of the National Museum of Canada were undertaken.

---

[1] See Barbeau, *Journal of American Folklore* 67:147–161 (1954). See Bibliog. 92.
[2] For references, see Barbeau, *Romancero du Canada,* 140 (Bibliog. 44).

As for *Les Roses blanches,* this canoe song was recorded first before 1930 by the singer Charles Marchand, and by Jean Lemieux and the author from Manitoba to Gaspé. It has been found since at various other points, but within Canada only—not in Acadia nor Louisiana—by other collectors, François Brassard and Carmen Roy.

Ballantyne, before all others, wrote about it as follows:

> . . . in the canoe, bounding merrily up the river (the Winnipeg river), while the echoing woods and dells responded to the lively air of *Rose Blanche* sung by the men as we swept round point after point and curve after curve of the noble river.
>
> I have seen forty canoes sweep round a promontory suddenly and burst upon my view, while at the same moment the wild romantic song of the *voyageurs,* as they plied their brisk paddles struck upon my ear; and I have felt thrilling enthusiasm on witnessing such a scene.
>
> With hearts joyful at the termination of their trials and privations, with all the force of three hundred manly voices, one of their lively airs, which rising and falling in the distance as it was borne, first lightly on the breeze, and then more steadily as they approached, swelled out in the rich tones of many a mellow voice, and burst at last into a long enthusiastic shout of joy. Away we went then, over the clear lake, singing *Rose Blanche* vociferously.

France has so far furnished only an incomplete version of this song; it was published by Barbillat and Touraine in their *Chansons populaires du Bas-Berry.* But we have heard of two others, one in Vincent d'Indy's songs from the Vivarais, and the other in Closson for French-speaking Belgium.

The prosodic pattern of this song is a familiar *pre,* that is, the lines are of fourteen syllables (8 + 6f), uniformly rhyming (*assonancés*) in *-an,* thus forming a single epic lay. The cæsura is masculine, on the ending, feminine. In a single variant there is a refrain, but not in the others.

## REFERENCES AND SOURCES

**Published:**

1. Barbeau, *Romancero,* 139–144 (Bibliog. 44) with a list of eight sources, from 1848 to 1930; locations: the Hudson Bay (the R. M. Ballantyne version), two versions from North Gaspé, two from Temiscouata, one each from Montmorency, Montcalm, and Saint Boniface (Manitoba).

2. ———, *Alouette!*, 26–28 (Bibliog. 59): "Le médecin de Nantes." There are five additional versions in the François Brassard collection, two from the Chicoutimi area, one each from Metabetchouan, Lake Saint John, and from Lévis, and one version in the Gustave Lanctôt collection from Orleans near Ottawa (quite different from the others).

3. Barbeau, *Folk Songs of Old Quebec*, 42, 43 (Bibliog. 40).

4. ———, *Aux armes, Canadiens!*, 7 (Bibliog. 49).

5. ———, *Come A Singing!*, 53 (Bibliog. 66).

**Sources:**

In addition to the thirteen versions above:

14–16. Collected by the author in 1941 from J. B. Dupuis, La Tourelle (Gaspé), in collaboration with Mrs. Laura Boulton in 1941; from Wilbrod Lavoie, Saint-Hilarion (Charlevoix); from Mme. Maurice Savard, Rang-Saint-Joseph (Tadoussac) in 1946, No. 4604.

17. Collected by François Brassard from Urbain Petit, Strickland, Ontario, in 1943.

18, 19. Collected by Carmen Roy, from Léon Collins, La Tourelle (Gaspé), *ca.* 1950, No. 5529; from Joseph Robison, Anse-Pleureuse (Gaspé), Nos. 5389, 5395.

# VOICI LE PRINTEMPS

## *THE SPRINGTIME IS COME*

## Voici le printemps

Voici le printemps,    la saison nouvelle,
Où tous les amants    changent de maîtresse.

*Le bon vin m'endort,*
*L'amour m'y réveille.*

Où tous les amants    changent de maîtresse.
Mais change qui voudra,    je garde la mienne.

Mais change qui voudra,    je garde la mienne.
Elle a les yeux doux,    la bouche vermeille.

114

Elle a les yeux doux,   la bouche vermeille.
Qu'il est bon d'avoir   un baiser d'elle!


## The Springtime Is Come

Oh! the springtime is come, when trees and flowers awaken,
And all our village bachelors new lady-loves have taken

*Tis good wine makes me sleep,*
*But love will me awaken.*

Though the lads of the village other loves have taken,
I'll never follow in their wake, and leave my love forsaken.

I will not like a traitor, leave my love forsaken.
So sweet the thoughts her gentle eyes and rosy lips awaken!

Oh! The sweet thoughts her eyes, and rosy lips awaken!
And what a dream of happiness the little kiss I've taken!


In France, where it was popular, we find this song along the Loire River valley, in Berry and Ille-et-Vilaine, also in Brittany, Franche-Comté, and even in Lorraine. But it seems not to have spread to the *langue d'oc* provinces to the south. In one of our Canadian versions, the tower of La Rochelle is mentioned (*Son cœur a été d'river du long de La Rochelle*). From this we may infer that it sailed from this western seaport to New France with the early colonists.

It must have come to Canada and Acadia with the seventeenth-century emigrants of the lower Loire River, who settled on the upper Saint Lawrence—Montreal and Three Rivers, not Quebec—and in Acadia, where the population was mostly from Poitou. And it has remained attached to its earthy roots to the present day.

This is a song of the soil (*du terroir*), and it revels in the bounties of the table and the delights of love-making. It sings of the rebirth of springtime—or, more precisely, in a variant, of the awakening of nature in the month of May. In its lyrical effusions it explores sensuous pleasures which are no longer politely expanded upon. For this reason we have had to omit a long ending, in spite of its engaging fancy.

*Voici le printemps* (Springtime is come) is not the only song of this variety. At least three of its parallels are known in Canada, Acadia, and France. They develop along similar lines, except for the tunes and refrains. For instance: "Voici le printemps que les fleurs nouvelles. . . . (Refrain): Moi, je sais quelque chose," or again, "Voici le printemps qu'est arrivé, tous les garçons se marient. . . . La et la la la. . . ." There are also two or three variants which begin with the same "Voilà le printemps," and branch off into other choruses: "Vogue, mon amant, vogue. . . . La lune s'en va," and, "Je l'ai vu voler, le ruban de la mariée." [1]

It is a rhythmic canoe and handicrafts song, with a single feminine rhyme or assonance, in the form of an epic lay in *-ai, -ei,* and *-è.* Its cæsura, inversely, is masculine. Its stanzas consist of twin lines followed by a refrain. As usually happens in this kind of ditty, the last line of a stanza is repeated in the following stanza, this being in turn the last and the first. It is very irregular modally. It is harmonized, here in A major, ending in the tonic minor.

## REFERENCES AND SOURCES

**Published:**

1. James H. Lanman, *Hunt's Merchants' Magazine,* Sept. 1840, p. 189. This article refers to Thomas Moore's "boat songs."

2. *Historical Collections of the Great West,* Cincinnati, 1855, vol. 1, 80, 81. These two references given by Prof. Joseph Médard Carrière.

3. In Barbeau, *Romancero,* six versions are listed, from 1916 to 1926, from the following areas: Beauharnois, Berthier-en-haut, Saint-Rémi-de-Napierville, Saint-Romuald (Lévis). The last four were collected by E. Z. Massicotte; one version was collected by Adélard Lambert, Berthier-en-haut; from the author's collection recorded with the singer, Edouard Hovington, Tadoussac, 1916 (Bibliog. 44).

4. Acadian versions, by Père Anselme and Frère Daniel Boudreau, Chéticamp, Cape Breton, in their *Chansons d'Acadie,* 3ème série, 1948 (Bibliog. 69).

5. *Ibid.,* 21.

6. Sœur Marie Ursule, in "Civilisation traditionnelle des Lavalois," *Les Archives de Folklore* 5–6:316, 317 (Bibliog. 83).

---

[1] Cf. Barbeau, *Romancero du Canada,* 48 (Bibliog. 44).

**Sources:**

In addition to the above eleven versions, the following Acadian items have been collected since by J. T. Le Blanc from Antoine Le Blanc, Central Ave., Norwich, *ca.* 1937, No. 9231; and from J. C. Boudreau (who was born in Chéticamp, Cape Breton) at Trois-Rivières, Quebec, No. 9232.

# LE TAMBOUR

## THE DRUM

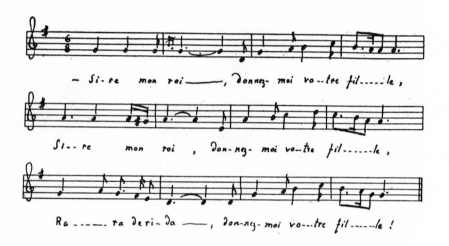

- Si-re mon roi——, donnez-moi vo--tre fil-----le,

Si--re mon roi , Don-nez- moi vo-tre fil------le,

Ra ------ ra de ri-da —— , don-nez- moi vo---tre fil-----le !

## Le Tambour

"Sire mon roi,   donnez-moi votre fille, (*bis*)

*Ra raderida*
donnez-moi  votre  fille!"

"Dis-moi, tambour,   où sont tout' tes richesses? (*bis*)
"Tout' mes richesses,   mon tambour, mes baguettes!" (*bis*)
"Va-t'en, tambour,   tu n'auras pas ma fille." (*bis*)
"J'ai trois navires   dessus la mer jolie, (*bis*)
"L'un chargé d'or   les autr' de marchandises. (*bis*)
"Le plus joli, .   c'est pour porter m'amie." (*bis*)

118

"Reviens, tambour,  je te donne ma fille." (*bis*)
"Je m'ris de vous,  de vous, de votre fille. (*bis*)
"Dans mon pays  yen a de plus jolies." (*bis*)
"Dis-moi, tambour,  dis-moi qui est ton père!" (*bis*)
"Mon père est roi,  il est roi d'Angleterre!" (*bis*)


## The Drum

"Hail gracious King!  I come to woo your daughter! (*bis*)


*Ra raderida*
I come to woo your daughter!"


"Drummer, declare,  declare to me your fortune." (*bis*)
"Here is my wealth,  my stirring drum and drumsticks." (*bis*)
"Drummer, begone,  you cannot have my daughter!" (*bis*)
"Three goodly ships  I have upon the ocean, (*bis*)
"One full of gold,  of merchandise another. (*bis*)
"One best of all,  shall bear my chosen lady." (*bis*)
"Drummer, return,  my daughter I will give you." (*bis*)
"Nay, haughty King!  I spurn you and your daughter. (*bis*)
"Fairer by far  the maidens of my country." (*bis*)
"Drummer, declare,  who is your noble father?" (*bis*)
"He is a king,  my father's King of England." (*bis*)


*Le Tambour* is one of the best-known songs in the whole French repertory. It figured nearly at the head of the list among Yvette Guilbert's favorites, but its tune and refrain as interpreted by this singer differed from the above variant.

As widespread in the motherland as in the New World, it has been published and recorded in North America in about thirty versions from Acadia, Canada, and Louisiana, as may be seen in the Bibliography and the Sources given below.

Its theme is a would-be royal marriage—or rather proposal—presumably between the French and English crowns. But the event failed to come off, as it did in other famous songs, such as *Le Mariage anglais*.[1]

## REFERENCES AND SOURCES

**Published:**

1. Healey Willan, in *French Canadian Folk-Songs*, vol. 2:6, 7; collected by the author, 6, 7 (Bibliog. 20).

2. Père Anselme and Frère Daniel, Acadians from Chéticamp, Cape Breton, in *Chansons d'Acadie*, 2ème série, 31 (Bibliog. 57); No. 4300, in the National Museum collection.

3. Irène Thérèse Whitfield, *Louisiana French Folk Songs*, 56–58 (Bibliog. 47).

4. François Brassard, *Les Archives de Folklore* 1:42 (Bibliog. 62).

5. Corinne L. Saucier, *Histoire et traditions de la paroisse des Avoyelles en Louisiane*, 438, 439 (Bibliog. 73).

**Sources:**

1. In "Annales musicales du Petit-Cap," notebook of Abbés Hamel and Doherty, Ms. 3, Archives du Séminaire de Québec, *ca.* 1860.

2. In the author's collection, from Edouard Hovington, Tadoussac, 1916, No. 424. Tune reproduced here.

3. In the E. Z. Massicotte collection, 1917–1918, from Mme. Alfred Malchelosse (née Eugénie Audet) at Laprairie.

4–9. In the author's collection, from Alcide Léveillé, Notre-Dame-du-Portage (Temiscouata), 1918, No. 1816; from Mme. Augustin Langlois, Port-Daniel, 1923; from Mme. Prudent (Adéline) Langlois, Port-Daniel, 1923 (twice recorded); from Mme. Paul Langlois (Emilie Michel) Port-Daniel, 1923; from Frank Deraîche, Port-Daniel, 1923, No. 3552; from Georges Bouchard, Rivière-au-Renard, 1923. His family originally came from Montmagny.

10. In the Adélard Lambert collection, from Berthier-en-haut, *ca.* 1918. Tune recorded by ear.

11. In the author's collection, from Napoléon Lachance, Saint-Ferréol, 1919.

12. In *Nos Vieilles Chansons, Programme souvenir* . . . [Anonyme], Montreal, 1928, 14.

13. In the Acadian collection of the Rev. P. Arsenault, Mont Carmel, Prince Edward Island. Melody recorded by the Rev. Gallant, *ca.* 1924.

---

[1] See George Doncieux, *Le Romancéro populaire de la France*, 303–311.

14. In the author's and Mrs. Regina Schoolman's collection at Cabano (Temiscouata), *ca.* 1935, from Joseph Mignault.

15.–17. In J. T. Le Blanc's Acadian collection, from Mme. Thomas Gauvin (Marcelline Doiron), Saint-Anselme, N. B., *ca.* 1938; published in *La Voix d'Évangéline,* Moncton, N. B., No. 9536; from Philippe Gaudet, Moncton, N. B., No. 9535; Another version, No. 9534.

18. In the François Brassard collection, from Mme. Charles Caron (Anna Pelletier), Jonquières, 1941. Tune recorded by ear.

19. In the author's collection, from Père Anselme and Frère Daniel, from Chéticamp, Cape Breton, in 1941, No. 4428. This version was published in *Chansons d'Acadie,* 2ème série, 31.

20, 21. In the manuscript thesis at Laval, 1944, of Gaston Eugène Adam, "Chansons françaises en Louisiane," two versions: 82, 83, 84, 85 (Bibliog. 100).

22. In the Carmen Roy collection, from Mlle. Angélique Parisé, of Paspébiac, in 1950, No. 5611.

23. In the Luc Lacourcière collection, from Majorique Duguay, 1951, at Pointe-Canot, Lamèque, N. B., No. 1103.

24. In the collection of Dr. Dominique Gauthier, from Mme. Jean Comeau, in 1953, at Evangéline, N. B., No. 9296.

# DANS LES PRISONS DE NANTES

## IN THE PRISON OF NANTES

Dans les prisons de Nan----tis, Dans les prisons de Nan---tis, luy ----at un pri--son ---nier ----. Gai faluron lurет----tε, luy ------at un pri--son--nier----. Gai faluron Don--Dé.

## Dans les prisons de Nantes

Dans les prisons de Nantes, (*bis*)

                      luy at un prisonnier,

    *Gai faluron lurette,*

                      luy at un prisonnier,

    *Gai faluron dondé,*

Que personn' ne va voire (*bis*)   que la fill' du geolier.

Un jour, lui porte à boire, (*bis*)   à boire et à manger.

"Contez-moi donc, la belle, (*bis*)   ce que l'on dit de moi!"

"Les bruits cour'nt dans la ville (*bis*)   que demain vous mourrez."

"S'il faut que demain j'meure, (*bis*)   détachez-moi les pieds."

Quand il eut les pieds lâches: (*bis*)   "Détachez-moi les mains."

122

Quand il eut les mains lâches, (*bis*)  à la mer s'est jeté.
A la première plonge, (*bis*)  a manqué s'y noyer.
A la deuxième plonge, (*bis*)  la mer a traversé.
A la troisième plonge, (*bis*)  à terre il a monté.
Quand il fut sur ces côtes, (*bis*)  il se mit à chanter.
"Que Dieu béniss' les filles, (*bis*)  surtout cell' du geolier.
Si je retourne à Nantes, (*bis*)  oui, je l'épouserai."


## In the Prison of Nantes

In prison cell at Nantes, (*bis*)
                                    a fettered captive lay.
            *Gai faluron lurette,*
                                    a fettered captive lay,
            *Gai faluron dondé.*
Alone the gaoler's daughter (*bis*)  came near him night or day.
She brought a cup of water, (*bis*)  a crust of bread he ate.
"Oh! tell me, gaoler's daughter, (*bis*)  what is to be my fate?"
" 'Tis rumored in the city (*bis*)  tomorrow you will die."
"If I must die tomorrow, (*bis*)  pray you my feet untie."
When she his feet had loosened, (*bis*)  "Untie my hands," said he.
When she his hands had loosened, (*bis*)  he plunged into the sea.
The first time he went under, (*bis*)  a drowning man was he.
The second time he struggled, (*bis*)  and struck across the sea.
He made a third endeavor, (*bis*)  and stood upon dry ground.
He stood, with strength recovered, (*bis*)  and sang a merry round.
"Of all God's gentle maidens, (*bis*)  the gaoler's child for me!
"If I return to Nantes, (*bis*)  yes! she my bride shall be."


This paddling and work song is one of the French and Canadian
favorites. Its origin, from its very title and in Doncieux's opinion,[1] is
presumed to go back to Nantes, in southern Brittany. Yet its locality
is London in most Canadian versions, of which more than thirty have
been recorded both in Acadia and Canada. Doncieux lists sixteen
for France, all from nothern provinces of *langue d'oïl*, mostly from

---

[1] Doncieux, *Le Romancéro populaire de la France*, 321–324, 501, 502.

123

Brittany; and Millien [2] quotes three more for the Nivernais—in all, about twenty for France against more than thirty for the New World.[3]

Its prosodic form is once more that of an epic lay, uniformly rhyming in -é or -ai. Its lines count twelve syllables (6f + 6) with a feminine epic cæsura at the sixth. A burden, as in most work and dancing songs, stands between the repetitions of the first hemistich of each stanza.

## REFERENCES AND SOURCES

**Published:**

1. *Nouvelle lyre canadienne, ou Chansonnier de tous les âges* (Anonyme), Montreal, 1858, 164–166.

2. LaRue, "Les chansons populaires et historiques du Canada," *Le Foyer canadien* 1:357 (Bibliog. 1).

3-6. Ernest Gagnon, *Chansons populaires du Canada*, 26–30; four tunes (Bibliog. 2).

7. William McLennan, *French Songs of Old Canada* (Bibliog. 5).

8. Loraine Wyman, "Songs from Percé," *Journal of American Folklore* 33:324, 325; tune recorded by Signor Betti (Bibliog. 12).

9. In *Chansonnier Allaire,* according to Abbés Biron and Fortier, 1947.

10. In the Acadian collection of Père Anselme and Frère Daniel, from Chéticamp, Cape Breton, in *Chansons d'Acadie,* 3ème série, 1948, 16, Nos. 4320, 4367 (Bibliog. 69).

11. Sœur Marie Ursule, "Civilisation traditionnelle de Lavalois," *Les Archives de Folklore* 5–6 (Bibliog. 83).

**Sources:**

1-5. In the author's collection, from Mme. Jean F. Bouchard, Éboulements-en-haut, 1916, No. 32; from J. G. Tremblay, 1916, No. 346; from Louis l'Aveugle, Saint-Irénée (Charlevoix), 1916, No. 179; from Edouard Hovington, Tadoussac, 1916, No. 430; from Ovide Souci, Saint-Antonin (Temiscouata), 1918, No. 1926.

6. In the J. T. Le Blanc Acadian collection, from Mme. Hervé Richard, Moncton, N. B., *ca.* 1938.

7. Collected by the author in 1946 from Malcolm Hovington, born in Tadoussac, No. 157. It was called *Chanson de rames.*

---

[2] A. Millien, *Chants et chansons populaires du Nivernais,* vol. 2, 46–49.

[3] F. R. Angers, *Recueil de chansons canadiennes et françaises,* 31, gives, as a "Chant de Voyageur Canadien," a form which may or may not be different from Gagnon's.

8. Barbeau, collected in 1948 from Mme. Adéline Landry, an Acadian born at Havre Aubert, Magdalen Islands.

9–11. Collected by Marcel Rioux in 1948 at Île-Verte (Rivière-du-Loup) in three versions: No. 4726 from Amédée Fraser; No. 4733 from Mme. Narcisse Levesque; and No. 4767 from Mme. Amédée Fraser.

12–17. In the Carmen Roy collection, from Antoine Clavet of La Madeleine (Gaspé), No. 5111b; three versions from Benoit Denis, Petit-Cap, 1951, Nos. 6524, 6525, 6573; from Johnny Landry, Saint-Omer (Gaspé) in 1950, No. 5711; from L. Collins, La Tourelle (Gaspé), No. 5711.

18. In the François Brassard collection, from Arthur Claveau, Chicoutimi, in 1941; "Exécutée súr l'eau. On ramait debout, à hanches, dans des chaloupes à voiles."

19, 20. In the collection of Dr. D. Gauthier, from Mme. Martin Le Breton, 1953, Shippigan, N. B., No. 9172; and from Vincent Vienneau, in 1953, Shippigan, N. B., No. G143.

21. In the collection of Luc Lacourcière and Sœur Marie Ursule, Laval, 1946, No. 208.

22, 23. In the Lacourcière-Savard collection, from Mme. Armand Bouchard, Baie-des-Rochers (Charlevoix), 1947, No. 281; another version from the same singer, 1947, No. 280.

24–26. In the collection of Luc Lacourcière, from Adélard Godbout, Saint-Raphael (Bellechasse), 1953, No. 1665; from Antoine Clavet, La Madeleine (Gaspé), in 1949, No. 733; from Ed.

27. In a Lacourcière-Barbeau recording, from Malcolm Hovington, formerly of Tadoussac, 1946, No. 157.

28. In the Lacourcière-Savard collection, from Mme. Armand Bouchard, Baie-des-Rochers, 1947.

# À SAINT-MALO

## AT SAINT-MALO

A Saint-Malo, beau port de mer, A Saint-Malo, beau port de mer, Trois gros na-vir's sont ar-ri-vés. Nous irons sur l'eau nous y prom' prom'ner, Nous i-rons jou-er Dans l'î----le, Dans l'î----le.

## À Saint-Malo

À Saint-Malo,   beau port de mer, (*bis*)
Trois gros navir's   sont arrivés.

> *Nous irons sur l'eau*
> *Nous y prom' promener*
> *Nous irons jouer dans l'île,*
> > *dans l'île.*

Trois gros navir's   sont arrivés (*bis*)
Chargés d'avoine,   chargés de blé.

126

Trois dam's s'en vienn'nt   les marchander. *(bis)*
"Marchand, marchand,   combien ton blé?"

"Trois francs, l'avoin';    six francs, le blé." *(bis)*
"C'est bien trop cher   d'un' bonn' moitié."

"Si j'le vends pas   j'le donnerai." *(bis)*
"A ce prix-là   faut s'arranger."


## At Saint-Malo

Here in the port of Saint-Malo *(bis)*
Hundreds of vessels come and go.

*Let us take a trip on the lovely ship,*
*We will walk and talk together,*
                    *together.*

See there are three with freight complete *(bis)*
Laden with barley, full of wheat.

Three women come the grain to buy, *(bis)*
"Trader, are prices low or high?"

"Barley is three francs, wheat six francs." *(bis)*
"Terribly dear! No thanks, no thanks!"

"Take it for nothing then, my friends." *(bis)*
"That's cheap enough to suit our ends."


But for this song the name of Saint-Malo might have long disappeared from the memory of Canadian country folk. Yet few towns in all France should mean so much to present-day Canadians. It was Jacques Cartier's home town, from which he sailed in 1534 for the discovery of Cathay—and came eventually to the Saint Lawrence. Individual recollections of the folk almost never pass on to posterity

127

unless embodied in some work of art, humble though it may be. Without that vehicle even the most momentous historical events fade away within a few generations.

But it is not as the port on the sea wherefrom remote forebears once sailed for the New World that Saint-Malo is here recalled to memory, for *At Saint-Malo* is not a pious hymn or a patriotic outburst. As an everyday work or canoe song, it merely tells of "vessels three" that "did come a-sailing, laden with oats and laden with wheat," and of "three ladies in the market street" approaching "to bargain groats."

Why is it that the song is so popular in Canada, where it is almost a national favorite? Popular caprice is not easily fathomed. Merry and smart though it is, the tune is by no means of exceptional merit; yet so eminent an authority as Julien Tiersot has declared it the best on record for the text.[1] The stimulus for the rebirth of this ditty may have been due, in the 1830s to the ferment of rebellion and to a pronounced racial awakening. The name of Saint-Malo, well-known to historians and politicians, may have sounded like a patriotic catchword, no matter what the contents of the song. So it was printed and rehearsed everywhere. "À Saint-Malo, beau port de mer" sounded like the name of a dear relative to most Canadians, though more than one-half of the pioneers, in fact, were not from Normandy but from the provinces of the lower Loire (Anjou, Poitou, Aunis, Berri); they had not sailed from Saint-Malo, but from La Rochelle on the west coast.

Oddly enough for a patriotic song, *At Saint-Malo* is not a lofty effusion, but a rather trivial narration of bold gallantry. The ending, now lost in Canadian versions, has been supplied from French records by Doncieux.[2] It runs as follows:

> 7  "Entrez, Mesdames, vous verrez!
> 8  La plus jeune a le pié leger,
> 9  Dedans le bateau a sauté.
> 10  Voilà que le vent a soufflé.
> 11  Le bateau s'est mis a voguer."

---

[1] G. Doncieux, *Le Romancéro populaire de la France,* . . . Avec un avant-propos et un index musical par Julien Tiersot.

[2] Doncieux (ibid., "Le bateau de blé et la dame trompée," 452–454) has compiled thirteen versions, chiefly from northwestern France, the birthplace of the song, to which may be added the earliest record for Canada, that of LaRue, *Le Foyer canadien* 1:338, 339, and that of Champfleury and Wekerlin, *Chansons populaires des provinces de France,* 156. Cf. also F. Arnaudin's "A Bordeaux . . ." in *Chansons populaires de la Grande-Lande et des régions voisines,* vol. 1, 159; and A. Millien, *Chants et chansons populaires du Nivernais,* vol. 2, 71, 72.

12 "Arrête, arrête, marinier!
13 Je suis femme d'un conseiller."
14 "Quand vous seriez femme du Roë,
15 Avec vous je coucherai."

And other versions from Bittany continue with the lines:

"Jamais enfant n'avez porté."
"S'il plaît à Dieu, vous en aurez
Avec un maître marinier!"

The name of Saint-Malo itself is not an essential feature of the song. We hear of the port of Nantes instead in three French records; and the authentic form, according to Doncieux, was no other than

Devant Bordeaux est arrivé. . . .

Printing and popular abuse in town and school have impoverished this canoe song to a much greater extent than they have *Roll my ball.* Interesting variants in tune and words were once found as well as in other folksongs; all traces of them have not yet disappeared. But most of the versions that may still be recorded in Quebec are identical, and the melody, shallow in the first place, has now grown stale and stereotyped. The present record, which we owe to the courtesy of Loraine Wyman of New York was obtained from Grégoire Quirion in 1918 in the neighborhood of Percé (Gaspé). It contains little, if anything, that differs from those previously published in Canadian songbooks.

## REFERENCES AND SOURCES

**Published:**

1. Barbeau and Sapir, *Folk Songs of French Canada,* "At Saint-Malo," 121–124 (Bibliog. 14).

2. Barbeau, *Alouette!,* 51–53 (Bibliog. 59).

3. *Nouvelle lyre canadienne, ou Chansonnier de tous les âges* (Anonyme), Montreal, 1856, 12, 13: "C'est dans la ville de Bordeaux."

4. H. LaRue, "A Saint-Malo," 338, 339 (Bibliog. 1).

5. Ernest Gagnon, *Chansons populaires du Canada,* 24, 25 (Bibliog. 2).

6. Loraine Wyman, "Songs from Percé," *Journal of American Folklore* 33:323, 324 (Bibliog. 12).

7. By Uldérie Allaire and several others.

8. Barbeau, *Aux armes, Canadiens!,* 3 (Bibliog. 49).

**Sources:**

In Barbeau, *Alouette!,* 53, are listed eight more versions of this song, as follows, according to date and location: Saint-Norbert (Berthier-en-haut), Sainte-Geneviève-de-Batiscan—these last two in the Massicotte collection; Saint-Irénée (Charlevoix), Cabano (Temiscouata), Sainte-Famille and Argentenay (Île d'Orléans)—the last three in the author's collection, Stokes (Eastern Townships)—in the collection of Jules Tremblay.

9, 10. One version and two tunes in the "Annales musicales du Petit-Cap," notebook of Hamel and Doherty, in Archives du Séminaire de Québec, Ms. 3.

11. Collected by the author and Mrs. Laura Boulton from Joseph Ouellet, La Tourelle (Gaspé), in 1941.

12. An Acadian version recorded by J. T. Le Blanc, from Mme. Octave Gagnon, Saint-Antoine, N. B., No. 9994.

Add

# LE BÂTIMENT MERVEILLEUX

## THE WONDERFUL BOAT

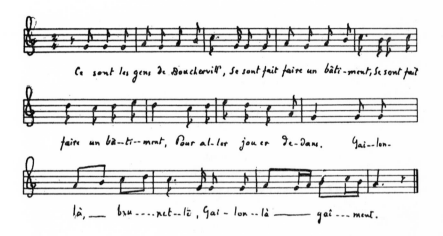

## Le Bâtiment merveilleux

Ce sont les gens de Boucherville
Se sont fait faire un bâtiment (*bis*)
Pour aller jouer dedans.

> *Gailonlà, brunette!*
> *Gailonlà, gaîment!*

La charpent' du bâtiment,
C'est un' boite de fer blanc.
Les trois mats du bâtiment,
Sont trois cotons d'herb' Saint-Jean.

131

Le gouvernail du bâtiment,
C'est la queue d'un vieux ch'val blanc.
Les trois voil's du bâtiment,
Sont trois vest's de bouragan.

Le capitain' du bâtiment,
C'est un vieux bœuf au front tout blanc.
La cuisinièr' du bâtiment,
C'est un' vach' de trente-cinq ans.

L'équipag' du bâtiment,
Ce sont des agneaux du printemps,
Et tous ceux qui vont dedans,
Ce sont de vrais innocents!


## The Wonderful Boat

The worthy folk of Butcher-town,
Determined they would build a boat;
Determined they would build a boat,
And would have some fun afloat.

> *Gailonlà, brunette,*
> *Gailonlà, gaîment!*

They made a start upon the hull:
For it an old tin box sufficed;
Three stalks of mugwort furnished masts
Rigged with halyards badly spliced.

The wondrous rudder was the tail
That once adorned an old white horse.
The sails that fluttered on the masts,
Three ton shirts of fustian coarse.

The captain of that man-of-war,
An old white-frontaled bull was he.

132

The cook that served that man-of-war
Was a cow aged thirty-three.

The crew were little springtide lambs
That gaily gamboled fore and aft.
And everyone aboard that ship
Was quite definitely daft.

This swaying canoe song belonged, like many others, to singers in the Montreal district whose forebears had been voyageurs and canoemen in the service of the North West and the Hudson's Bay companies. They used to sing whole days on the wild rivers in their search for pelts among the Indian hunters of the Great Lakes and the prairies.

E. Z. Massicotte, the author's collaborator (1917–1929), recorded it for the National Museum from one of the best singers in the country, whose repertory was salvaged in the last years of his life. Folk singers, as we have known and consulted them, had a vast hoard of recollections. Among them was Vincent Ferrier de Repentigny, born at Beauharnois, who alone gave Massicotte about 300 items; Philéas Bédard of Napierville and Joseph Rousselle from Saint-Denis (Kamouraska) both produced nearly 200. And the best of all, François Saint-Laurent of La Tourelle (Gaspé) recorded with the author 310 songs, besides a number of folktales and legends.

The name of Boucherville in the present song is merely a misnomer; it is not enough in itself to lead us to believe that the song was composed within its borders, on the shore of the upper Saint Lawrence. One fine day some canoeman of this village conferred upon it the nostalgic name of his own birthplace. The song itself, like countless others, is from an old French source. It belongs to a familiar type of wonder stories or fantastic lies. Let's lie with gaiety, and something real and true will be left behind! This one, *The Wonderful Boat,* could not fail to bring both sidesplitting laughter amid the gurgling waters of the rapids.

There is no essential modulation in the tune itself until the end, where it definitely goes to the relative minor.

This song of Vincent Ferrier de Repentigny of Beauharnois recalls another which may have inspired its composition, before the Canadian name of Boucherville was first introduced. This other is not only of better quality but is also older. It came from the Rev. P. Arsenault, the Acadian curate of Mont Carmel, Prince Edward Island (in 1924):

133

"C'est les filles du Hâvre/Qu'ont fait faire un bâtiment./Ils l'ont fait bâtir corsaire/Pour aller à l'île aux Vents. . . ." The lines of this last composition are of fourteen syllables, with epic cæsura (7f + 7). *Le Bâtiment merveilleux*, its derivative, follows the same prosodic pattern for the first line only, and also the epic cæsura; then it definitely adopts the masculine rhyme in *-an*, as in an epic lay.

## REFERENCES AND SOURCES

**Published:**

1. P. E. Prévost, *Chansons canadiennes*, 68 (Bibliog. 6).
2. E. Z. Massicotte and M. Barbeau, *Journal of American Folklore* 32:73, 74 (Bibliog. 10).
3. Barbeau, *Alouette!*, 68, 69 (Bibliog. 59).
4. ———, *Aux armes, Canadiens!*, 34, 35 (Bibliog. 49).
5. Père Anselme and Frère Daniel, *Chansons d'Acadie*, 3ème série, 1, 2 (Bibliog. 69).

**Sources:**

1–6. Six versions are listed in *Alouette!*, 70; they belong to the Massicotte, Père Archange, and the author's collections, and are from Lévis, Nicolet, Belœil, Saint-Anselme (Dorchester), Saint-André Kamouraska). A version was sent to the author by L. P. Geoffrion from Varennes; another came from Saint-Pierre les Becquets.

7. The Massicotte collection contains a version from Pierre Lavallée, recorded at Saint-Norbert (Berthier), 1926: "Les habitants de Saint-Martin. . . ."

8. In the Marcel Rioux collection, from Joseph Levesque, Île-Verte, 1948, No. 4808: "Les habitants de Charlesbourg. . . ."

9. In the J. T. Le Blanc Acadian collection, published in *La Voix d'Evangéline*, from Philippe Gaudet, Moncton, No. 9983.

10. In the Carmen Roy collection, from Léon Collins, La Tourelle (Gaspé), 1950, Col. 162. Melody transcribed by the author. (Bibliog. 102, p. 272.)

# JE LUI PRIS SA MAIN BLANCHE

## *I TOOK HER BY HER WHITE HAND*

## Je lui pris sa main blanche

Après ma journé' faite,
  *Et tra et tra et tralire lanlire,*
Après ma journé' faite,   il est temps de s'en aller,
  il est temps de s'en aller. (*bis*)
Dans mon chemin rencontre . . . une fille abandonnée.
Je lui pris sa main blanche, . . . dans ma chambr' l'ai emmené'.
"Déshabillez-vous, la belle, . . . dans mon lit vous coucherez."
"Mais, ma robe est trop petite, . . . mon corset est fort noué."
"Mon épée est sur la table, . . . prenez-la et dénouez."
La belle a pris l'épée, . . . droit au cœur se l'est passé'.

135

Voilà donc m'ami' morte, . . . il faut la faire enterrer.
Faut fair' venir le prêtre . . . pour chanter son *Libera.*
Aux quatr' coins de sa fosse . . . le rossignol a chanté.


## *I Took Her by Her White Hand*

After the day was over,
              *Et tra et tra et tralire lanlire,*
After the day was over,   homeward I took my way,
              homeward I took my way. *(bis)*
Strolling alone a maiden . . . straight across my path did stray.
By her white hand I took her . . . into my chamber gay.
"You must disrobe, my beauty, . . . lie you down and rest, I pray!"
"Nay, but my dress fits closely, . . . knotted very tight my stay."
"Here with my sword, my beauty, . . . you can cut the knotted stay."
Then with my sword that maiden . . . pierced her heart and passed
   away.
Since she is dead, poor sweetheart, . . . I must dig her grave today.
So let the priest be sent for, . . . he must now her requiem say.
Over the tomb the nightingale, . . . sang a little roundelay.


The first record of this Canadian and Acadian song confers upon it the name of *Chanson métisse,* that is, *Half-breed Song,* for what reason no one knows, because it has not been recorded in the Northwest, where the *métis* (part-white and part-Indian) lives, on the western prairies.

Yet, in a broader sense, it really is a half-breed song. It embodies two contrasting features of European songs, in particular those of France. Its theme is that of a *complainte,* or tragic narrative, wherein death is recorded; it is also a come-all-ye of the type familiar in all the northern countries of Europe, England, Scandinavia, etc., and also in northern France, where the *langue d'oïl* dialects are spoken. But it is not traditional in southern France, where the *langue d'oc* dialects are spoken, nor in any of the Latin areas to the south. In a word, northern Europe is given to narratives or concrete stories, whereas the south, where ancient civilizations linger, practices lyric tune and poetry or abstractions.

Lyrical songs include all types of verse and lines and their subjects are universal. Rhythmical and partial to the dance and work motions, they tend to be lilting and lively.

The theme of *Je lui pris sa main blanche* belongs to the north of Europe but its treatment here is southern. It has been forced, as it were, into the vestment of a work and dancing song. Tragic though it was to begin with, it developed an air of gaiety which is artificial while traveling southward into Poitou and the lower Loire country of the early Candian emigrants.

## REFERENCES AND SOURCES

**Published:**

1. In *Le Droit,* Ottawa, March, 1922, communicated by Gustave Lanctôt, and described as "chanson métisse." Like the version presented here, it begins with "Voilà la journée faite," but it ends differently.

2. It was recorded for the first time in full by the author from Mme. J. B. Leblond, at Sainte-Famille (Island of Orleans) in 1925, No. 4051.

3. Recorded by Mrs. Laura Boulton and the author in 1941, at Baie-Saint-Paul from Mme. Onésime Lavoie—a dance song.

4, 5. In the J. T. Le Blanc collection, from Mme. Joseph Léger, Moncton, and published in *La Voix d'Evangéline, ca.* 1938, No. 9397; and from Philippe Gaudet, Moncton, No. 9980.

6. In the Lacourcière-Barbeau collection, from Mme. Jean Goulet, Saint-Pierre (Island of Orleans), *ca.* 1945, Nos. 51 and 4503.

7–9. In the Carmen Roy collection, from Octave Minville, La Tourelle (Gaspé), *ca.* 1948, No. 4895: "Par un dimanche au soir, A Longueuil. . . . ;" from Baptiste Denis, Rivière Morris (near Rivière-aux-Renard), No. 2423; from Mme. Zéphirin Dorion, Port-Daniel, 1950, No. 5833.

# C'EST L'AVIRON QUI NOUS MÈNE

## COMING BACK HOME

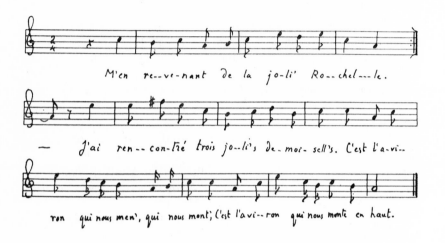

M'en re-ve-nant de la jo-li' Ro-chel---le. — J'ai ren--con-tré trois jo--li's de-moi-sell's. C'est l'a-vi-- ron qui nous men', qui nous mont', C'est l'avi--ron qui nous monte en haut.

### C'est l'aviron qui nous mène

M'en revenant    de la joli' Rochelle, (*bis*)
J'ai rencontré    trois joli's demoisell's.

*C'est l'aviron qui nous mèn', qui nous mont',*
*C'est l'aviron qui nous monte en haut.*

J'ai rencontré    trois jolies demoiselles. (*bis*)
N'ai pas choisi,    mais j'ai pris la plus bell'.

N'ai pas choisi,    mais j'ai pris la plus belle. (*bis*)
Je l'ai monté    avec moi sur la selle.

138

Je l'ai monté  avec moi sur la selle. (*bis*)
J'ai fait cent lieues  sans parler avec elle.

J'ai fait cent lieues  sans parler avec elle. (*bis*)
Après cent lieues,  ell' me demande à boire.

Après cent lieues,  ell' me demande à boire. (*bis*)
Je l'ai conduit  tout droit à la rivière.

Je l'ai conduit  tout droit à la rivière. (*bis*)
Quand elle y fut,  ell' ne voulut point boire.

Quand elle y fut,  ell' ne voulut point boire. (*bis*)
Je l'ai conduit  tout droit dessur son père.

Je l'ai conduit  tout droit dessur son père. (*bis*)
Quand ell' fut là,  ell' buvait à plein verre.

## Coming Back Home

As I was coming back from fair Rochelle, O, (*bis*)
I came upon three pretty demoisell's.

> *It is the paddle that drives the canoe,*
> *It is the paddle that moves us on.*

I took away the prettiest of the three, (*bis*)
And mounted her upon my horse with me.

One hundred leagues in silence did we ride, O, (*bis*)
When suddenly, "I want a drink," she cried.

I led her quickly to the river's brink, O, (*bis*)
But when I got her there, she would not drink.

I took the damsel homeward by and by, O, (*bis*)
And then she drank and drained a beaker dry.

139

Just like Saint-Malo, Bordeaux, Nantes, Marseille, and Toulon, the port of La Rochelle in France yielded its name to the minstrels (*faiseurs de dicts*) who were partial to thrilling sea adventures. In such affairs, too often gallant, the gay mariners set foot ashore and kidnaped maidens who imprudently lent an ear to their advances. Again, they tarried at the seaport because of flirtations at times too indiscreet for words—even with the president's wife (*la femme du président*)—and for brimful libations. And they were given to turning their experiences into rhymes and ditties.

Rabelais himself, who knew not a few folksongs of the western provinces where he belonged, links up his Dindonneau to La Rochelle. This fictitious character, a sheep trader at sea, met his ruin at the hands of Gargantua. But here the author of *Pantagruel* called the city port La Lanterne (from the clock in the belfry with a huge lantern which was well known to sailors); and this name currently applied to the seaport near the mouth of the Loire River.

By a curious inversion in the present song, La Rochelle or La Lanterne comes into the picture not as the gate to the high seas, but merely as a place of rendezvous for an inland knight who brushes right past the sea captains, captures a pretty girl they must have coveted, and ravishes her on horseback. The maiden, as spotless as she is beautiful, would not utter a word, even though very close to him for 100 leagues in the saddle no less. The polite horseman, bent on courtesies, lets her down close to a clear fountain by the path, where a love denouement is usually facile. Vain hope: she would not drink a drop!

In chivalry, one may expect a good turn, first of all the improbable. Here this high-bred rider yields to the maiden's desire to be escorted forthwith to her father's lodge, in the country nearby. But why, in the first place, had she run away to La Lanterne! To end up, the wench, in front of her whole kin, splits her sides with laughter and drinks cupfuls of wine to the health of her gallant rescuer. Why? Because, too timid, he had not dared!

Here is the stuff out of which the lay has been fashioned, for again it is expressed in the form of an epic lay, 4 + 6f, with uniform assonances in -*è*, and invertly, masculine cæsuras.

*M'en revenant de la jolie Rochelle* has traveled without much injury along the huge rivers of the New World, on the parched lips of canoemen and *coureurs de bois*. So doing it has earned its Canadian epaulets, as it were. It has come to enjoy the reputation of being one of the gayest voyageur songs.

Popular as it is in some regions, and often included with at least two different tunes in songbooks, still it remains unknown in most parts. It was seldom met with on the lower Saint Lawrence. It proved a useful paddle song up the rivers and down the rapids in the North-west, in the "pays d'en haut." But it also has turned up in the Maritimes among the Acadians, perhaps because of their Poitevin ancestry, close to the port of La Rochelle.

This should be compared with *The Baffled Knight*, Child #112. The same type also turns up in Percy's *Reliques*.

## REFERENCES AND SOURCES

**Published:**

1. Ernest Gagnon, *Chansons populaires du Canada,* "En revenant de la jolie Rochelle," 155, 156 (Bibliog. 2).
2. E. Z. Massicotte, *Le Canard* (Montreal), 1897, 3.
3. P. E. Prévost, *Chansons canadiennes,* 111 (Bibliog. 6).
4. Julien Tiersot, *Songs of the People,* 76–78 (Bibliog. 7).
5. J. M. Gibbon, *Canadian Folksongs,* 58–60 (Bibliog. 17).
6. Père Anselme and Frère Daniel, *Chansons d'Acadie,* 1ère série, 15, No. 4362 (Bibliog. 50).
7. Barbeau, *Alouette!,* 15–18 (Bibliog. 59).
8. ———, *Come A Singing!,* 51 (Bibliog. 66).
9. François Brassard, from Urbain Petit, Strickland, Ont., 1946, in *Les Archives de Folklore* 1:54–57 (Bibliog. 62).
10. ———, from *L'Alma Mater* (Chicoutimi), Dec. 1944, 78.
11. ———, No. 3, Jan. 1950, 65.

**Sources:**

1–6. In the author's *Alouette!* are listed four other versions collected (1918–1941) by him, E. Z. Massicotte, J. T. Le Blanc, and Ernest Sylvestre, from Notre-Dame-du-Portage, Berthier-en-haut, Lamèque in N. B., and Sainte-Anne-de-Richelieu.

7. Collected by Mrs. Laura Boulton from Blanche Cimon, Baie-Saint-Paul, in 1941.

8. By Carmen Roy in 1950, from Léon Collins, La Tourelle (Gaspé), No. 5605.

# ELLE ÉTAIT BELLE, ELLE LE SAVAIT

## SHE WAS LOVELY, SHE KNEW IT

C'est dans Pa--ris, yat: u----ne bru--ne. Elle é--tait
belle, ell' le — sa-vait. Pas besoin qu'on lui dis', Voyez-vous! J'ai-me lon-
la malon--la malu-ret--te, J'aime lon-la malonla ma-lu-ré.

### Elle était belle, elle le savait

C'est dans Paris,   yat une brune,⎤
Elle était belle,   ell' le savait.  ⎦ *(bis)*

> *Pas besoin qu'on lui dis',*
> *Voyez-vous!*
> *J'aime lonla,*
> *Malonla malurette,*
> *J'aime lonla,*
> *Maluron maluré.*

Elle était belle,  ell' le savait.  ⎤
Lorsque son amant va la voir,  ⎬ *(bis)*
   *Un baiser lui demand',*
   *Voyez-vous!*

"Un doux baiser,  c'est pour en rir'."  ⎤
"Prenez-en un, prenez-en deux,  ⎬ *(bis)*
   *Passez-en votre envi'!*

Prenez-en un,  prenez-en deux,  ⎤
Galant, passez-en  votre envi'.  ⎬ *(bis)*
   *Si papa le savait,*

Car si mon papa le savait,  ⎤
Du gros bâton  j'en goûterais.  ⎬ *(bis)*
   *Ma mère, elle sait bien.*

Quant à ma mère,  elle sait bien.  ⎤
Elle ne fait  jamais qu'en rir'.  ⎬ *(bis)*
   *Son amant lui demand',*

Mais quand son amant lui demand'  ⎤
Un doux baiser,  c'est pour en rir'.  ⎬ *(bis)*
   *D'un signe de la têt',*

D'un sign' de tête  elle refus',  ⎤
Mais de la main  ell' le retient,  ⎬ *(bis)*
   *Car son cœur lui dit Oui!*

Je sais si bien  ce qu'ell' faisait,  ⎤
Dans le bon temps  qu'elle était fill'.  ⎬ *(bis)*
   *Elle se savait bell'."*


## She Was Lovely, She Knew It

Lived a brunette in gay Paree.  ⎤
Lovely she was, as she'd agree.  ⎬ *(bis)*
   *Plainer it could not be.*

*Do you see?*
*Lara lonla malonla malurette,*
*Lara lonla maluron maluré.*

Lovely she was as flowers in May,⎤
She knew it well, no need to say.⎦(*bis*)
    *Came her young man one day,*

Came her young man to call one day.⎤
"One little kiss for fun, I pray,      ⎬(*bis*)
    *Come along, don't say nay!*

One sure enough, but why not two?"⎤
"All that you please, then off with you,⎬(*bis*)
    *But suppose father knew.*

For if my father only knew,         ⎤
Surely he'd beat me black and blue.⎦(*bis*)
    *Mamma would wink at you.*

Mamma would wink instead of blame.⎤
She'd only smile, the sly old dame;  ⎬(*bis*)
    *Her lover does the same.*

When her young man says, 'Please, a kiss,⎤
One or two more won't come amiss,'      ⎬(*bis*)
    *Mother just nods like this,*

Wagging her head to answer 'No,' ⎤
Holding his hand, she won't let go.⎦(*bis*)
    *Mothers a-plenty know,*

Mother knows what she used to do,   ⎤
When she was young like me and you:⎬(*bis*)
    *Once she was lovely too."*

This song for handicrafts is frolicsome and is perhaps better known now in France than in Canada, because the Paris singer Yvette Guilbert has made it famous everywhere. She ascribed her French version to a western province in France—at Parthenay. It was one of the jewels of her repertory.

In Canada alone—not in Acadia or Louisiana—it has come down to us only in the present form without variants, in all only four times. Here it appears as recorded from François Saint-Laurent, an outstanding Gaspé singer and fisherman.

The first two lines in each stanza consist mostly of eight syllables (*pieds*) with a cut at the fourth, adopting the same prosodic pattern as *Les trois canards blanc, À Saint-Malo,* and others. The third line of the stanza (this type of verse is exclusively in the folk vein) is shorter; it contains only six syllables. As to the rhymes or assonances, our frivolous ditty seems to look for none. Perhaps this is merely an oversight or simply due to the shortcomings of folk memory. The folk keep dropping features of their heirlooms.

As for the tune, it sways to the cadence of 6/8, in the major mode. Everybody now is partial to this form and gradually forgets the older modes that were just as lovely if not more so, but which now have become archaic.

### REFERENCES AND SOURCES

**Published:**

1. Conrad Gauthier, "40 chansons d'autrefois," 76, 77 (Bibliog. 38).
2. Barbeau, *Alouette!*, 41, 42 (Bibliog. 59).

**Sources:**

1–3. In the author's *Alouette!* is given a list of three versions recorded at La Tourelle (Gaspé) in 1918: by E. Z. Massicotte, at Saint-Cuthbert—"A Lanoraie, il y avait. . . ." and by Adélard Lambert at Berthier-en-haut.

# JE SAIS BIEN QUELQUE CHOSE
## *I KNOW A THING OR TWO*

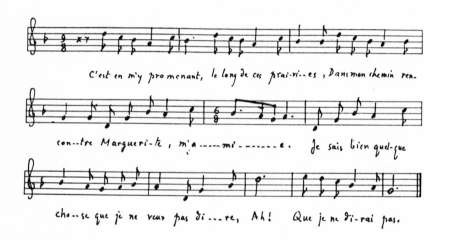

C'est en m'y promenant, le long de ces prai-ri--es, Dans mon chemin ren-
con--tre Marguerite, m'a------mi--------e. Je sais bien quel-que
cho--se que je ne veux pas di----re, Ah! Que je ne di-rai pas.

### Je sais bien quelque chose

C'est en m'y promenant,   le long de ces prairies,
Dans mon chemin rencontr'   Marguerite m'amie.

*Je sais bien quelque chose*
*Que je ne veux pas dire,*
*Ah!*
*Que je ne dirai pas.*

"Qu'avez-vous à soupirer,   Marguerite, m'amie?"
"Ne sais-tu pas, galant,   que mon père m'y marie?

146

Ne sais-tu pas, galant,   que mon père m'y marie?
A un vieillard bonhomm'   qui a la barbe grise?

Je voudrais que ces vieux   soient dedans un navire,
A cinq cents lieues au larg',   sans pain et sans farine,

Pour leur montrer par là   pucelles à poursuivre.
Les vieux sont pour les vieill's,   les garçons pour les filles."


## I Know a Thing or Two

As through the fields I walked   merry was I to meet her,
She is the girl I fancy,   my Marguerite, none sweeter.

> *I know a thing or two,*
> *A thing or two I do,*
> *But ah!*
> *I'll never tell it you.*

"Tell me, my Marguerite, why weeping here you tarry?"
"Do you not know that father tells me that I must marry?

I am to have a bridegroom   grizzled and weak and silly;
Whether I want or no, I   must take him willy-nilly.

What a good thing 'twould be if   all these old men were taken
Many miles out to sea to   starve and to die foresaken!

Let the old men have crones,   maidens they should not tether.
Crabbèd old age and youth   never can live together."


In times past ambitious parents arranged for their daughters to
espouse wealth rather than to marry for love. And wealth, alas! meant
old age, if not avarice. The Marguerite of our canoe song bitterly
resents this practice. She would have the aged husbands doomed to
live on bread and water, 500 leagues out to sea—hers like the rest, or
better still, the first of them all.

147

In this state of mind, a young bride who takes a sweetheart into her confidence is already well on the path to secret consolation. Should you doubt it, lend an ear to the burden, and you get the clue: she know a thing or two which she won't tell, Oh! This secret (of infidelity, no doubt) she shares with many other *maumariés* of former times.

The lines of twelve syllables, with a cæsura at the sixth, are alternately, in halves, masculine and feminine, all aligned in a single lay with -*i* for assonance. This soft ending betrays the gentility of the complainte. A woman, even when she scolds, never betrays her sex. The bitterness she feels for her old chief melts into sweetness when she turns to her confidant, who never fails to lend an ear and live up to expectations.

This song belongs especiallly to the lower Saint Lawrence River. But it is also, in some form or other, current in the motherland. Rolland gives two variants from Vendée and the neighborhood of Lorient. Fouquet has recorded one from Morbihan in Brittany; Beauquier has found it farther afield in Franche-Comté. And last, "Mon père m'a donné un mari" was first printed in *L'Harmonice Musices Odtrecaton* of Petrucau, of 1501–1503.[1]

## REFERENCES AND SOURCES

**Published:**

1. Sir Ernest MacMillan, *Vingt-et-une chansons canadiennes,* 15, 16 (Bibliog. 19).
2. Barbeau, *Alouette!,* 65–67 (Bibliog. 59).

**Sources:**

Of the five versions (1918–1925) recorded by the author and listed in *Alouette!,* two came from Saint-André (Kamouraska), one each from Notre-Dame-du-Portage (Temiscouata), La Tourelle (Gaspé), and Saint-François Nord (Island of Orleans).

---

[1] Rolland, *Recueil de chansons populaires,* vol. 1, 77–78. His version from Vendée comes from the Mss. B. Nat., VI. 449. Beauquier, in *Chansons populaires recueillies en Franche-Comté,* 269: "La peau à Paris." A. Fouquet, *Légendes, contes et chansons de Morbihan,* 156: "Écorcher les vieux maris." Petrucau, *Mélusine* 4:49.

# LA MARIÉE S'Y BAIGNE

## *THE COBBLER WHO WENT OUT TO SEE THE LADIES*

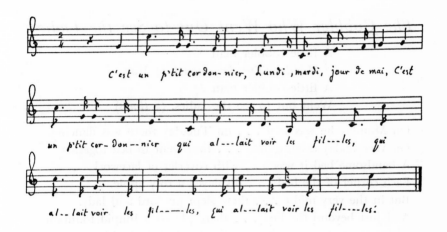

C'est un p'tit cordon-nier, Lundi, mardi, jour de mai, C'est un p'tit cor-Don--nier qui al---lait voir les fil---les, qui al--lait voir les fil----les, qui al---lait voir les fil----les:

## La Mariée s'y baigne

C'est un p'tit cordonnier,
> *Lundi, mardi, jour de mai,*
C'est un p'tit cordonnier,   qui allait voir les filles,
> qui allait voir les filles. (*bis*)

En brodant ses souliers, . . . il a fait la demande.
Son père le veut bien, . . . sa mère en est contente.
N'y a que les parents . . . qui font face dolente.
Murmure qui voudra, . . . aux amours faut se rendre!
Le lundi, c'est les noc's, . . . le mardi c'est la danse.

149

Le mercredi au soir, . . . ils coucheront ensemble,
Dans un beau lit carré, . . . couverture en dentelle.
Aux quatre coins du lit, . . . quatre pommes vermeilles.
Mais au chevet du lit, . . . le verre et la bouteille.
Au beau milieu du lit, . . . le galant et la belle.
A la tête du lit, . . . le rossignol y chante.
Tout à côté du lit, . . . une claire fontaine.
C'est là que, le matin, . . . la mariée se baigne.
Elle s'y est tant baigné, . . . qu'elle a perdu ses peignes,
Ses peignes et ses atours, . . . ses atours et ses peines.


## The Cobbler Who Went Out to See the Ladies

A little cobbler man
*Monday, Tuesday, month of May,*
A little cobbler man
Went out to see the ladies. (*3 times*)

On Monday he was wed . . . on Tuesday there was dancing.
On Wednesday evening late . . . they went to bed together.
A handsome bed it was . . . with coverlet of lacework.
Each corner of the bed . . . displayed a rosy apple.
But in the very midst . . . there slept my lord and lady.
And just beyond the bed . . . there played a limpid fountain.
There every day you saw . . . the lovely lady bathing.
She bathed so very long . . . her comb fell in the water.
And so she bathed again . . . till she her comb recovered.


This gay paddling and work song traveled all over western America with the voyageurs and canoemen. Marking the rhythm of the paddles, it whipped up the spirits of tired workers and brought enchantment to their imaginations as they kept longing for home and sweet love. Its rhythm was resorted to whenever in the rapids of wild rivers the paddles had to accelerate their strokes. And the mode of C major, here so sunny, helped to banish melancholy.

Why should a shoemaker, a commonplace man, be the favorite in this venturesome proposal, a man whom the parents of the sweetheart would no doubt consider undesirable? For a shoemaker, of all the ancient craftsmen, was the one least likely to wed a beauty. His efforts were vain when he tried to maneuver her into a bed gorgeously bedecked, at the edge of a clear fountain.

Censorship would defeat itself if it were to frown upon such outbursts in songs as this in *La Mariée s'y baigne* and *Avec son aiguille*, on p. 83, which belong together but follow a different path in their development. For the voyageurs must be pardoned for their frivolity, considering that they were journeying under great difficulties at times, under burning sun or cold rain, stung by mosquitoes and bitten by the winds. Meanwhile they would dream of a bed of roses and the crystal fountain of their gratified love, where the nightingale sang for joy.

In two-lined stanzas (*distiques*), with the second line repeated, is inset a refrain which evokes the enchantment of May and springtime. The lines consist of 6 + 6f = 12 beats, like the classical alexandrines. But the whole piece itself is in the form of an epic poem with uniform feminine rhymes or assonances in *-an, -è*, or *-ei*.

This paddling and work song is widely known, as can be ascertained in the appended list. It belongs to Acadia as well as to Quebec, up and down the Saint Lawrence and around the Gaspé coast.

## REFERENCES AND SOURCES

**Published:**

1. Barbeau, *Le Soldat canadien chante*, 32, 33 (Bibliog. 48).

2. ———, *Alouette!*, 54, 55 (Bibliog. 59).

3, 4. Père Anselme and Frère Daniel, *Chansons d'Acadie*, 3ème série, 42, 43; two tunes recorded (Bibliog. 69).

**Sources:**

1–3. Three versions are listed in the author's *Alouette!*, 56, as coming from E. Z. Massicotte in 1917, for Beauharnois (tune reproduced here); in 1919 from Longue-Pointe; and from the Arsenault Acadian collection, Mont Carmel, Prince Edward Island, in 1926.

4. In the Massicotte collection, a version from Sainte-Geneviève-de-Batiscan, in 1917.

5, 6. Recorded by J. T. Le Blanc from the "cahier de Mme. Fred Saint-Pierre de Landry Office, N. B." *ca.* 1938; No. 9066 at the National Museum; from Mme. François Allain, of Saint-Antoine, N. B., No. 9067.

151

7. Recorded by Frére Marcellin-André Simonneau, from Rosaire Groulx, in 1946, at Sainte-Thérèse-de-Blainville (Terrebonne).

8. Recorded by Lacourcière and Barbeau at Quebec, from Eusèbe Thurbide, in 1947. Thurbide was an Acadian from the Madeleine Islands. The tune was recorded by Alfred Pouinard.

9. Recorded by Mlle. Pierrette Cousineau in Montreal in 1947.

10. Collected by Marcel Rioux in 1948 from Mme. A. Parent, Île-Verte (Rivière-du-Loup) No. 4734.

11. By D[ucasse] from Claude Bilodeau in 1954.

12–15. The Carmen Roy collection from Mme. Antoine Castonguay, Rivière-à-Claude, *ca.* 1950, No. 5004; from Baptiste Denis, Rivière Morris (near Rivière-au-Renard) No. 540; from Léon Collins, La Tourelle, in 1951, No. 6507; another version from the same region, No. 5561.

# PAS TROP CONTENT

## HM, HM, SULKY AND CROSS!

Par un ma-tin, p'tit Jean s'lè-ve, hm hm hm, mais pas trop content, Par un ma--tin, p'tit Jean s'lè-ve, Prend sa hach', s'en vat au bois. Prend sa hach', s'en vat au bois, Prend sa hach', s'en vat au bois.

### Pas trop content

Par un matin, p'tit Jean s'lève

*Hm, hm, hm,*
*Mais pas trop content,*

Par un matin, p'tit Jean s'lève,
Prend sa hache, s'en vat au bois. (*ter*)

P'tit Jean a dit à sa femme: . . .
"Mon dîner m'apporteras!" (*ter*)

Voilà le midi qui sonne . . .
Le dîner n'arrive pas. (*ter*)

153

P'tit Jean a jeté sa hache, . . .
Descendit à la maison. (*ter*)

"Tiens, p'tit Jean, voilà ta soupe, . . .
Dans ta soup', ton lard salé." (*ter*)

Quand p'tit Jean mangeait sa soupe, . . .
Sa chatte emporta son lard. (*ter*)

"Si je m'en prends à ma chatte, . . .
La gueuse m'égratignera. (*ter*)

Si je m'en prends à ma femme, . . .
Le curé me grondera. (*ter*)

Il vaut bien mieux laisser faire, . . .
Que de mener le cabat." (*ter*)


## Hm, Hm, Sulky and Cross

Little John got up one morning,

*Hm, hm, hm,*
*Sulky and cross.*

Little John got up one morning,
Took his ax into the wood. (*3 times*)

Little John told his old woman, . . .
"You will bring my lunch to me." (*3 times*)

But the hour of midday sounded, . . .
And the lunch did not arrive. (*3 times*)

Little John threw down his hatchet, . . .
In a rage back home he went. (*3 times*)

154

"Little John, your soup's all ready, . . .
And your piece of ham as well." (*3 times*)

Little John his soup was lapping . . .
When the cat ate up the ham. (*3 times*)

"If I try to punish pussy, . . .
Then the horrid beast will scratch. (*3 times*)

If I swear at my old woman, . . .
I shall risk the curé's wrath. (*3 times*)

Better far to take things easy . . .
Than to rouse a sleeping dog." (*3 times*)

This other *maumarié* song—the pair does not get along at all well together—presents a wife who is not keen in the fulfillment of her domestic duties. In other skits of this kind, she saves the best dishes for a favorite whose identity is only hinted at, in the absence of the husband.

Songs of this class—fortunately or otherwise—are quite numerous. Alas for the characters at play, their trials are not confined to literature! But in folklore they are a constant object of mockery and fun. So their ill luck serves a purpose.

P'tit Jean, a Charlevoix woodsman, submits here to his lot, which, after a hard day's toil, mean a piece of salted pork for supper. He is a fatalist. Who knows? At other times he may have thrashed the wife as she deserved, only to be preached at by the parish priest or scratched by the cat.

Charlevoix is the tag attached here to this lumberjack song only because it was recorded in 1916 with Louis l'Aveugle at Saint-Irénée. This noted singer and folktale teller is the singer who more than any other in Canada reminded us of the ancient jongleurs of provincial France. At sixty-five years of age, he was still trudging from place to place, a fiddle under his arm, glad to entertain whomever happened along and always ready to lend an ear. His cane was his antenna; it read the road for him like an open book. At one time, they say, he used a *bioune* (German harp) to accompany his tunes. It is now kept as a relic of other days at the museum of Séminaire de Chicoutimi.

Although journeying from house to house, he was not a common beggar by any means; but like his forerunners, he enjoyed certain rights which were hereditary. If he really had no fixed abode—except in the winter—he owned no less than two countries to exploit in his own way. And he gave back plenty for the fare he received. His listeners trooped around him and avidly listened by the hour, sometimes all night, to his chants, rigmaroles, and yarns. Everywhere he was most welcome and he practiced the axiom that "the door is on the latch." In France, it runs in reverse: Open the door, and you are welcome inside!

This work song is both Canadian and Acadian. It seems never to have been recorded before 1916. The twin lines consist of seven syllables each. The first has an uttered feminine ending; the second is masculine. The burden is in two parts, inside and outside. The part outside or final is the repetition of the second line. The first part of the tune is in C major, but its final phrase is in the mode of G.

## REFERENCES AND SOURCES

**Published:**

1. Barbeau, *Le Soldat canadien chante*, 16, 17 (Bibliog. 48).
2. ———, *Aux armes, Canadiens!*, 16, 17 (Bibliog. 49).
3. ———, *Alouette!*, 77, 78 (Bibliog. 59).

**Sources:**

1–5. Five versions are listed in the author's *Alouette!*, 79, 80, from the Barbeau and Le Blanc collections (1916–1941), of which two are from Charlevoix, one each from Verchères, Orléans (near Ottawa), and Middle Caraquet, N. B.

6. The collection of Frère Marcellin-André Simonneau of Sainte-Thérèse-de-Blainville (Terrebonne), from Rosaire Groulx, 1946: "C'était un p'tit bonhomme."

7–10. The Luc Lacourcière and Savard collection, from Mme. Philéas Morneau, Baie-des-Rochers (Charlevoix), 1947, No. 289; another version, No. 288; from Adélard Godbout, Saint-Raphael (Bellechasse), 1953, No. 1671: "Le grand faucheur."

11, 12. The collection of Dr. Dominique Gauthier, from Mme. Patrick Godin, 1952, Evangéline, N. B.: Nos. G60, "Un petit bonhomme qui s'en allait couper du bois," and G61, "C'est un tout p'tit bonhomme, youppe. . . ."

13. The D[ucasse] collection, from Augustin Gallant of Saint-Alexis (Matapédia), 1954. Refrain: "Pione . . . tralala."

# L'ÂNE DE JEAN

## JOHNNIE'S DONKEY

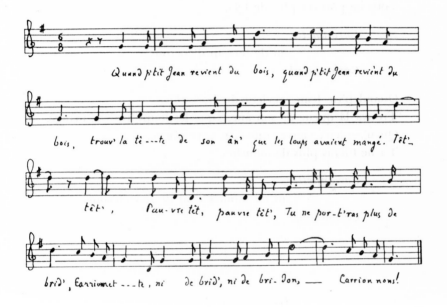

## L'Âne de Jean

Quand p'tit Jean   revient du bois, (*bis*)
Trouv' la tête de son ân'   que les loups avaient mangé.
Têt', têt', pauvre têt', pauvre têt',
Tu ne port'ras plus de brid',

   *Carionnette*
            ni de brid', ni de bridon,
   *Carionnons!*

Quand p'tit Jean   revient du bois, *(bis)*
Trouva le dos de son âne,   que les loups avaient mangé.
Dos, dos, pauvre dos, pauvre dos,
Tu ne porteras plus de selle,

> *Carionnette*
>> ni de sell', ni de sel'ron,
> *Carionnons!*

Quand p'tit Jean   revient du bois, *(bis)*
Trouva les patt's de son âne,   que les loups avaient mangé.
Patt's, patt's, pauvres patt's, pauvres pattes,
Vous ne port'rez plus de fers,

> *Carionnette*
>> ni de fers, ni d'éperons,
> *Carionnons!*

Quand p'tit Jean   revient du bois, *(bis)*
Trouva la queue de son âne,   que les loups avaient mangé.
Queu', queu', pauvre queu', pauvre queue,
Tu ne tueras plus de mouches,

> *Carionnette*
>> ni de mouches, ni de mouch'rons,
> *Carionnons!*

## Johnnie's Donkey

Coming from the wood one day, *(bis)*
Johnnie found his donkey's head
Which the wolves had gnawed away.
Head, head, poor old head, poor old head!
No more bridle will you wear,

> *Fol de rol ay-dee,*
>> neither bridle nor bridoon,
> *Diddle-dee-dey.*

Johnnie came from the wood one day, (*bis*)
Found his donkey's poor old back
Which the wolves had gnawed away.
Back, back, poor old back, poor old back!
No more saddle will you bear,

> *Fol de rol ay-dee,*
>
> never saddle great or small,
>
> *Diddle-dee-dey.*

Johnnie came from the wood one day, (*bis*)
Found his donkey's poor old hoofs
Which the wolves had gnawed away.
Hoofs, hoofs, poor old hoofs, poor old hoofs!
No more shoes you'll ever wear,

> *Fol de rol ay-dee,*
>
> never spurs again you'll feel,
>
> *Diddle-dee-dey.*

Johnnie came from the wood one day, (*bis*)
Found his donkey's poor old tail
Which the wolves had gnawed away.
Tail, tail, poor old tail, poor old tail!
No more flies you'll whisk away,

> *Fol de rol ay-dee,*
>
> no more gnats you'll whisk away,
>
> *Diddle-dee-dey.*

*L'âne de Jean* is a rigmarole or cumulative song of the same type as *Alouette* and *Le Merle* (The Blackbird), songs familiar in Canada. It belongs to the valley and the estuary of the Saint Lawrence exclusively. Seventeen versions were recorded after 1917, three of which have been published, the first as early as 1860.

This type is most ancient, not only in France but all over Europe. In many other folk forms, and they are numerous, we meet with an enumeration or an accumulation of items or events. At the end of each stanza, there is a return to the first items in the list.

Some of these rigmaroles once were mnemonic exercises to aid memory in keeping mysteries and the symbols of the faith. Some scholars have stated that they go back to Celtic times, others, that they are counted among Jewish chants in medieval times.

*Johnnie's Donkey* lays no claim in itself to being archaic, or even ancient. Nonetheless, it came to Canada—it seems to be unknown in Acadia and Louisiana—from the motherland with the colonists. Its triviality did not keep it from being a favorite among the voyageurs and canoemen as they coursed the rivers in America. It marked the motion of the paddle or the oars with a lilt.

To Loraine Wyman, a talented American *diseuse* and a disciple of Yvette Guilbert, we owe its first Canadian record, in 1918, at Percé (Gaspé). Miss Wyman in the early years took an interest in the progress of folklore research in Canada, and she was the best interpreter of *Veillées du bon vieux temps* on a series of programs at Montreal and elsewhere in 1919. This was the first of a series of public events wherein Canadian folksongs were raised, as it were, to the level of art music.

## REFERENCES AND SOURCES

**Published:**

1. Barbeau, *Veillées du bon vieux temps,* 51, 52 (Bibliog. 9).
2. ———, *Aux armes, Canadiens!,* 14, 15 (Bibliog. 49).
3. ———, *Alouette!,* 81, 82 (Bibliog. 59).
4. Sœur Marie Ursule, in "Civilisation traditionnelle des Lavalois," *Les Archives de Folklore* 5–6:346, 347 (Bibliog. 83).

**Sources:**

1. The "Annales musicales du Petit-Cap," Archives du Séminaire de Québec, notebook of Hamel and Doherty, *ca.* 1860: "Quand le mari s'en vient du bois."

2–12. In the author's *Alouette!* are listed ten versions, in the collections of Loraine Wyman, Barbeau, Massicotte, Lambert (1918–1942); two are from Percé and two from La Tourelle (Gaspé), one each from Portage (Temiscouata), Saint-Maxime (Dorchester), Lévis, Saint-Constant (Laprairie), Berthier-en-haut, and Orléans (near Ottawa); another is from Alcide Léveillé, at Notre-Dame-du-Portage (Temiscouata), 1918, No. 1787.

13. The collection of E. Z. Massicotte, from V. F. de Repentigny, Beauharnois, No. 867.

14. The author's and Mrs. Laura Boulton's collection, in 1941, from Mlle. Blanche Cimon, Baie-Saint-Paul.

15. Carmen Roy's collection, from Léon Collins, La Tourelle (Gaspé), *ca.* 1952, No. 5495.

# MARIANNE S'EN VAT AU MOULIN

## *MARY ANN GOES TO THE MILL*

Ma - ri - ann' s'en vat au moulin, Ma - ri - ann' s'en vat au moulin. C'est pour y fai - re moudre son grain. C'est pour y fai - re moudre son grain. A che-val sur - son â - - ne, Ma p'tit' Mamsell' Mari- anne, A - che-val sur son â-ne Ca--tin, Pour al-ler au moulin.

## Marianne s'en vat au moulin

Mariann' s'en vat au moulin, (*bis*)
C'est pour y faire moudre son grain, (*bis*)
    À cheval sur son âne,
    *Ma p'tit' mamsell' Marianne,*
À cheval sur son âne Catin,
    Pour aller au moulin.

Le meunier qui la voit venir *(bis)*
S'empresse aussitôt de lui dire: *(bis)*
 "Attachez donc votre âne,
 *Ma p'tit' mamsell' Marianne,*
Attachez donc votre âne Catin,
 Par derrièr' le moulin."

Pendant que le moulin marchait, *(bis)*
Le beau meunier la caressait. *(bis)*
 Le loup a mangé l'âne,
 *Ma p'tit' mamsell' Marianne*
Le loup a mangé l'âne Catin,
 Par derrièr' le moulin.

Marianne se mit à pleurer. *(bis)*
Cent écus d'or lui a donnés, *(bis)*
 Pour acheter un âne,
 *Ma p'tit' mamsell' Marianne,*
Pour acheter un âne Catin,
 Pour venir au moulin.

Son père qui la voit venir *(bis)*
S'empresse aussitôt de lui dire: *(bis)*
 "Qu'avez-vous fait d'votre âne,
 *Ma p'tit' mamsell' Marianne,*
Qu'avez-vous fait d' votre ân' Catin,
 En r'venant du moulin?"

"Mon père a bu du vin nouveau. *(bis)*
Mais qui lui trouble le cerveau. *(bis)*
 Ne r'connaît pas son âne,
 *Ma p'tit' mamsell' Marianne,*
Ne r'connaît pas son ân' Catin
 Qui me porte au moulin."

"Mon âne a les quatre pieds blancs, *(bis)*
Les deux oreilles rabattant, *(bis)*
 Le bout de la queue blanche,
 *Ma p'tit' mamsell' Marianne,*

Le bout de la queue blanch' Catin,
    En r'venant du moulin."

"C'est aujourd'hui le saint Michel, (*bis*)
Où tous les ân's changent de poil. (*bis*)
    Voilà c'qu'a fait votre âne,"
    *La p'tit' mamsell' Marianne,*
"Voilà c'qu'a fait votre ân' Catin,
    En r'venant du moulin."


## Mary Ann Goes to the Mill

'Twas Mary Ann rode down the hill, (*bis*)
To grind her barley at the mill, (*bis*)
    A-riding on her donkey,
    *O little Mary Ann,*
A-riding on her donkey Bill,
    A-riding to the mill.

The miller, when he saw the maid, (*bis*)
Politely bowed to her and said, (*bis*)
    "Now please tie up your donkey,
    *O little Mary Ann,*
Just tie up Billy where you will,
    Somewhere behind the mill."

Now when the wheel began to move, (*bis*)
The miller and the maid made love, (*bis*)
    A wolf ate up the donkey,
    *O little Mary Ann,*
He gobbled it up and ate his fill,
    Somewhere behind the mill.

Then Mary Ann began to cry. (*bis*)
Said he, "A hundred francs will buy, (*bis*)
    Will buy another donkey,
    *O little Mary Ann,*

In place of that the wolf did kill,
    Somewhere behind the mill."

Her father, when he saw the maid, *(bis)*
Made much ado and to her said, *(bis)*
    "What happened to the donkey,
    *O little Mary Ann?"*
"Why here it is, you must be ill!
    I rode it from the mill.

"My father, was the wine too strong? *(bis)*
Has something in your head gone wrong, *(bis)*
    That you don't know your donkey
    *Or little Mary Ann?*
Why surely here's your donkey still,
    I rode it from the mill."

"My donkey's feet were white, not black, *(bis)*
It had long ears a yard set back. *(bis)*
    My donkey's tail was piebald,
    *O little Mary Ann,*
That is not Bill, say what you will,
    Returning from the mill."

"Today you know is Michaelmas, *(bis)*
When new hides grow on every ass. *(bis)*
    That happened to your donkey,"
    *Said little Mary Ann,*
"For he's the same old donkey Bill
    That took me to the mill."

Very well known in France, this charming song is equally popular
in French America. It has been recorded many times in Canada and
also at old Vincennes (southern Indiana). The donkey (*âne*) of France
is called Martin, whereas in Canada, it is Catin. Donkeys, as Gagnon
remarks, were known here only through oral tradition, like the song
that sings of its misadventure while his mistress collects gold coins
from the miller inside the mill. The tune is modern and probably
without variants, which shows its rather recent date.

# REFERENCES AND SOURCES

**Published:**

1. Ernest Gagnon, *Chansons populaires du Canada,* 121–123 (Bibliog. 2). Gagnon's version has been reproduced in print by Rivard, Yon, Rowen, Gascoigne, Morin, Allaire, Biron, and A. Fortier.

2. Cecilia Ray Berry, *Folk Songs of Old Vincennes,* 76, 77 (Bibliog. 64).

3. Peggy Stack and Elizabeth Harding, *French Songs for Children,* 18. "L'âne de Marion" (Bibliog. 96).

**Sources:**

1. E. Z. Massicotte published a version in *Le Canard,* Montreal, Aug. 1896, 3.

2. It was recorded by the author from Mme. Jean Bouchard, Éboulements-en-haut, in 1916, No. 84, and is reproduced here.

Add

# LA POULE À COLIN

## COLIN'S HEN

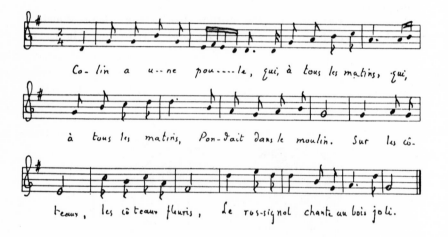

Co-lin a u-ne pou----le, qui, à tous les matins, qui, à tous les matins, Pon-dait dans le moulin. Sur les cô-teaux, les cô teaux fleuris, Le ros-signol chante au bois joli.

## La Poule à Colin

Colin a une poule   qui, à tous les matins,
Qui, à tous les matins,   pondait dans le moulin.

*Sur les côteaux,*
*Les côteaux fleuris,*
*Le rossignol chante,*
*Au bois joli.*

Colin a pris sa fourche,   lui a cassé les reins.
A fait une giblotte,   le dimanche au matin.

166

Invita tout le monde,   Nicolas, son voisin . . .
Le curé du village   y vint saucer son pain.

Trouva la sauc' si bonne   qu'il s'y est mis les mains;
Des mains, mais jusqu'aux coudes,   des coudes jusqu'aux reins.

A fait manquer la messe   à tous ses paroissiens.
S'il est monté en chaise   c'est pour prêcher Colin.

"Excusez, mes chers frères,   car je n'y suis pour rien.
Si vous manquez la messe,   c'est la faute à Colin!"


## Colin's Hen

Oh! Colin had a good fat hen who, every blessed day,
Who, every blessed day, a good fat egg would lay.

> *Where down the dell,*
> *Bloom the flowers of spring,*
> *Sweet nightingale,*
> *In the wood does sing.*

But Colin took a stout Maypole and broke her back in two,
And chose that Sabbath morn to make a chicken stew.

Then he invited everyone, and neighbor Nicol too.
The curé dipped his crust into the savory stew.

He found the stew so very good, his fingers deeper strayed,
His elbow got submerged, and soon his shoulder blade.

The parish missed its Sunday Mass, but though the hour was late,
He to the pulpit climbed and preached at Colin straight.

"Dear brethren, pray you pardon me, 'tis not for nought I came.
If you have missed your Mass, 'tis Colin is to blame!"

167

This smart ditty is both Canadian and Acadian and exists in more than twenty recorded versions. It falls back upon a favorite theme in French, that of the parishioner—he or she—and the curate. Satire bores its way in as a worm does into cheese. Never mind the irreverence; it is tolerated in the best families, and even a curate may be heard whispering it unbeknown to his vicar.

A song of this type—and there are not a few—derides a little the upper class for its pretense of learning and the use of books. Some of these songs are stuffed with Low Latin; others drop the Latin for English equivalents. This song in some versions flaunts another burden: "Blow in the morning, blow!"

Its twin-line stanzas, with epic cæsuras—these are mutes, which are articulate—rhyme uniformly in *-in* and form an epic lay, as often happens in this book. This traditional pattern in jongleur songs does not dampen their gaiety. The tune here is on a lilting 2/4, and continues throughout in a modern C major key.

## REFERENCES AND SOURCES

**Published:**

1. Conrad Gauthier, "40 chansons d'autrefois," 30, 31 (Bibliog. 38).

2, 3. Barbeau, *Le Soldat canadien chante* and *Aux armes, Canadiens!* (Bibliog. 48, 49).

4. ———, *Alouette!*, 60–62 (Bibliog. 59).

5. Père Germain Lemieux in *Folklore Franco-Ontarien*, 40, 41 (Bibliog. 74).

6. Sœur Marie Ursule, "Civilisation traditionnelle des Lavalois," 326, 327 (Bibliog. 83). It was recorded by Luc Lacourcière at Sainte-Brigitte-de-Laval, from Mme. Célestin Thomassin, No. 236.

**Sources:**

1–13. Thirteen versions are listed in the author's *Alouette!* They are in the collections of the author, Massicotte, and Lambert (1918–1941), and are from Notre-Dame-du-Portage (Temiscouata), Saint-François Nord (Island of Orleans), Saint-François (on the same island), Port-Daniel (Chaleur Bay), Sainte-Marie (Beauce), Beauharnois, Saint-Rémi-de-Napierville (two versions), Saint-Cuthbert, Berthier-en-haut, Orléans (near Ottawa), Drummondville, etc.

14, 15. Recorded by J. T. Le Blanc from Mme. François Allain, Saint-Antoine, N. B., *ca.* 1940, No. 9075; and from Marie Le Blanc, Haute-Aboujague, N. B., in 1940, No. 9077.

16. Recorded by the Rev. Saint-Raymond-Marie, Pensionnat des Saints-Anges, Saint-Jérôme (Assomption), 1945.

17. Recorded by Marcel Rioux from Mme. Henri Fraser, Île-Verte, 1948, No. 4710.

18. Recorded by Jean Lindsay, from Ludger Sigouin, of Mont-Tremblant, *ca.* 1950.

19, 20. The Carmen Roy collection, from Mme. Grégoire Langlois, of Petite-Madeleine (Gaspé), and Léon Collins, La Tourelle (Gaspé), *ca.* 1950, Nos. 5134, 5134b.

# AH! QUI ME PASSERA LE BOIS?

## WHO WILL PROTECT ME THROUGH THE WOOD?

Ah! qui me passe---ra le bois, moi qui-suis si pe-ti-te. Ce s'ra mon-sieur que voi--là, Car il a bon--ne mi-ne, La! Sommes-nous au mi-lieu du bois, Sommes-nous à la ri--ve?

### Ah! qui me passera le bois?

Ah! qui me passera le bois,   moi qui suis si petite?
Ce s'ra monsieur que voilà,   car il a bonne mine.

*Là!*
*Sommes-nous au milieu du bois,*
*Sommes-nous à la rive?*

Mais quand ils fur'nt passés le bois,   la bell' se mit à rire.
"Qu'avez-vous, bell', qu'avez-vous,   qu'avez-vous à tant rire?"

"Je ris de toi, je ris de moi,   de nos foll's entreprises.
D'avoir traversé le bois   sans petit mot me dire!"

"Oh! revenez, bell', revenez,   je vous donn'rai cent livres."
"Ni pour cent, ni pour deux cents,   ni pour trois, ni pour mille!

Ni pour un cent, ni pour deux cents,   ni pour trois, ni pour mille!
Fallait plumer la perdix   tandis qu'elle était prise!"


## Who Will Protect Me Through the Wood?

Who will protect me through the wood?   I am so young and tender.
That young man whose looks I like,   he'll be my brave defender, O.

> *Now we are halfway through the wood,*
> *Now we are well outside it.*

When they had passed the wood, she laughed,   she found the joke too
    funny.
"What's the matter? Tell me, pray!   Why laugh so loud, my honey?
    O."

"Laughing at you, I laugh at me,   for when we two went walking,
As we strolled across the wood,   neither of us was talking, O."

"Come away back, my likely lass,   a hundred pounds I offer!"
"Not for twice or thrice that sum   or any bribe you proffer, O.

Not for a thousand pounds! You've missed   your market altogether.
When you had the bird in hand   you should have plucked its feath-
    ers, O."


This graceful paddle song was first published in 1858, one of the
earliest in Canada. Ernest Gagnon, our pioneer, heard it about 1860
while crossing Lake Saint Pierre on the Saint Lawrence below
Montreal. Its melody is usually modal, although the singers at times
modernize it, as they often do in this and other songs. They are not
impervious to the influence of present-day music. The song is known

in France (as Gagnon observes) and is not widely diffused in the New World, although it has been recorded both in Canada and Acadia.

Its prosody consists of eight- and six-syllable lines, alternating, and a brief burden *Ah!* It may also be considered as being of sixteen syllables (8 + 8f), with a feminine assonance in *-i* throughout, which makes of it an epic lay.

## REFERENCES AND SOURCES

**Published:**

1. [Anonymous], *Nouvelle lyre canadienne, ou chansonnier de tous les âges,* 162–163.

2. Ernest Gagnon, *Chansons populaires du Canada,* 90–93 (Bibliog. 2).

3. Philippe-Aubert de Gaspé, *Mémoires,* 179; only the first stanza (Bibliog. 3).

4, 5. Julien Tiersot, *Songs of the People,* 2 versions, 66–69 (Bibliog. 7).

6. Père Anselme and Frère Daniel, *Chansons d'Acadie,* 3ème série, 33 (Bibliog. 69).

**Sources:**

1. The author's collection. The version reproduced here is from a record temporarily mislaid.

2. Luc Lacourcière, from Lazare Hudon, 1943, from Hébertville (Lac Saint-Jean), No. L37.

# JE LE MÈNE BIEN, MON DÉVIDOIR

## *CLEVERLY MY REEL I PLY*

Mon pèr' n'avait fil--le que moi, Je le mè ne bien, mon dé-vi-
Doir. Encor' sur la mer il m'envoie, Je le mè-ne bien, je le mène au
Doigt, je le mè ne bien, je le mène au doigt, je le mène bien, mon dé-vi-Doir.

### Je le mène bien, mon dévidoir

Mon pèr' n'avait fille que moi.
    *Je le mène bien, mon dévidoir.*
Encor' sur la mer il m'envoi'.
    *Je le mène bien, je le mène au doigt, (bis)*
    *Je le mène bien, mon dévidoir.*

Le marinier qui m'y menait,
Il devint amoureux de moi.

"Ma mignonnette, embrasse-moi!"
"Nenni, monsieur, je n'oserais,

Car si mon papa le savait,
Fille battu' ce serait moi."

"Mais qui, la belle, le lui dirait?"
"Sont les oiseaux qui vol' en l'air."

"Les oiseaux de l'air parlent-ils?"
"Ils parlent quand ils sont appris;

Ils parlent français aussi."
"Grand Dieu! que les homm's sont badins!"


## Cleverly My Reel I Ply

My father had no girl but me.
  *Cleverly my wheel and reel I ply.*
Why did he send me off to sea?
  *What a handy girl at the reel am I! (bis)*
  *Cleverly my wheel and reel I ply.*

The man who bore me off to sea,
Fell very much in love with me.

"Give me a kiss, my maiden fair!"
"No. No. No. No. I would not dare!

For if my papa ever knew,
He soon would beat me black and blue."

"But who would tell the tale of love?"
"The little birds that fly above."

"Have little birds the power of speech?"
"It all depends who's there to teach.

They French or Latin speak with ease."
"Great heav'ns, how human folk can tease!"

This spinning song, *Cleverly My Reel I Ply,* is widely traveled, as may be seen in the list below, and has been published many times since 1863. It is one of the best known in Canada, Acadia, and Louisiana. It is widely familiar, too, in the variant of the maid sent out to sea, whom the captain tries to kiss. She refuses because of the birds; they might tell, for they speak French and Latin, too. The song is nonetheless French to the core, in spite of its having survived only in French America.

It is obviously a woman's song, just as others, like *Les Trois dames de Paris* in the same category, belong to men. It must have been heard countless times in the garret, where the loom, reels, and spinning wheels were busily humming in springtime and summer, and in the kitchen during the winter. These were the seasons when spinning and weaving for the whole family were done, especially by the older generation. The folk singer Bédard appropriated it and gave it to E. Z. Massicotte, our Montreal folklorist and collaborator. While singing it he imitated the motions of an old woman twisting the yarn between her fingers and laying it on the reel (*dévidoir*).

Our forerunner, Ernest Gagnon, in his book *Chansons populaires du Canada,* states that it was also a favorite of canoemen when paddling. His singer from Maskinongé told him that he had heard it as early as 1820, when rivermen accompanied the governor, Lord Dalhousie, and his cheerful escorts ascending a river on the upper Saint Lawrence. "I still visualize," said he, "the slender oars painted red, dipping into or emerging from the clear water, to the cadence of *Je le mène bien."* The Sorel boatmen escorting the governor were, in goodly numbers, none other than the voyageurs of the Northwestern fur trade.

The prosodic pattern of this song consists, like many others, of twinline stanzas plus a burden. Each line is in two halves, with a masculine cæsura. Its rhymes appear in two sets, first *-ai* or *-oi,* and second, *-i,* thus presenting two epic lays in miniature. Its lovely melody is modal, in A, with the tonic also on the same note.

## REFERENCES AND SOURCES

**Published:**

1. LaRue, *Le Foyer canadien* 1:342 (Bibliog. 1).
2–5. Ernest Gagnon, *Chansons populaires du Canada,* "Sautez mignonne Cécilia," "Mon cœur est en âge," etc., 31–36; "Mon dévidoir," 31–36, 181, 182 (Bibliog. 2).

6. William McLennan, *French Songs of Old Canada* (Bibliog. 5).

7. P. E. Prévost, *Chansons canadiennes*, 61 (Bibliog. 6).

8. Barbeau, *Veillées du bon vieux temps*, 48, "Cécilia" (Bibliog. 9).

9. Gustav Lanctôt, "Chansons et rondes de Laprairie," *Journal of American Folklore* 33:336 (Bibliog. 13).

10. Barbeau and Sapir, *Folk Songs of French Canada*, 111–115 (Bibliog. 14).

11. Conrad Gauthier, "40 chansons d'autrefois," 74, 75 (Bibliog. 38).

12. Barbeau, *Romancero*, "Je le mène bien, mon dévidoir," 155–158 (Bibliog. 44).

13. Père Anselme and Frère Daniel, "Cécilia," in *Chansons d'Acadie*, 1ère série; National Museum, No. 4357 (Bibliog. 50).

14. Cecilia Ray Berry, *Folk Songs of Old Vincennes*, 54, 55 (Bibliog. 64).

15. François Brassard, *Les Archives de Folklore* 1:57–59: "Canot d'écorce" (Bibliog. 62).

16. Barbeau, *Alouette!*, 141, 142: "Tradelidelidelum" (Bibliog. 59).

17. Père Germain Lemieux, in *Folklore Franco-Ontarien*, 22, "Capot de capot" (Bibliog. 74).

**Sources:**

1–4. Four versions of this song under its *dévidoir* refrain are listed in Barbeau, *Romancero*, 158 (Bibliog. 44) as collected by Barbeau, Massicotte, and Lambert in Temiscouata, and Berthier-en-haut, and once at Saint-Rémi-de-Napierville.

5. Recorded by the author at Éboulements (Charlevoix) in 1916, from Elizabeth Tremblay, No. 22.

6. Recorded by J. T. Le Blanc from Mme. Narcisse Poirier, at Block 14, N. B., about 1940: "Cécilia."

7–9. The author and Laura Boulton, from Josaphat Lemay, at Orléans (near Ottawa) in 1941; three tunes with refrains taken down.

10. Georges Saint-Aubin, from A. Lavallée and Florian Guitard, from the Quebec region and Lachute, in 1942.

11. Luc Lacourcière from Lazare Hudon, at Hébertville (Lake Saint John) in 1943.

12. P. Gérard Blanchard, o.m.i., an Acadian version learned from a Gaspésian in 1944.

13, 14. François Brassard, in *L'Alma Mater*, November, 1945, p. 39; and September–October, 1946, p. 19: "Canot d'écorce."

15–17. Luc Lacourcière, from Philéas Morneau, Baie-des-Rochers (Charlevoix) in 1947, No. L292: "Mon driton, dritaine"; from Octave

Br . . . , in 1949, at Sainte-Marie-Salomé (Joliette) , No. L672: "Canot d'écorce"; and from the same singer, 1949, No. L674: "Montant driton lanlire."

18. François Brassard, in *L'Alma Mater,* Nos. 9, 10, October–November, 1951, p. 162: "Les oiseaux du bois parlent-ils?"

Add

# LA FONTAINE EST PROFONDE

## THE WELL IS DEEP

M'en vas à la fon-tai------ne, M'en vas à la fon---

tai---ne, pour rempli mon cru------chon, Don Don-dai ne

Don! pour remplir mon cru---chon, don--dai---ne, dondai----ne!

## La Fontaine est profonde

M'en vas à la fontaine (*bis*)   pour remplir mon cruchon,

> *Don dondaine don,*
>    pour remplir mon cruchon,
> *Dondaine, dondaine!*

La fontaine est profonde, (*bis*)   me suis coulée à fond,
Un cavalier s'arrête, (*bis*)   un cavalier barron.
"Que donneriez-vous, belle, (*bis*)   si j'vous tirais du fond?"
"Tirez, tirez," dit-elle, (*bis*)   "après ça, nous verrons."
Quand la belle fut à terre, (*bis*)   s'enfuit à la maison,
S'assit sur la fenêtre, (*bis*)   compose une chanson.

"Ce n'est pas ça, la belle, (*bis*)   que nous vous demandons:
Votr' petit cœur en gage, (*bis*)   savoir si nous l'aurons."
"Mon petit cœur en gage (*bis*)   n'est pas pour un barron.
C'est pour un homm' de guerre (*bis*)   portant la barbe au menton."


## The Well Is Deep

I took my pail one morning (*bis*)   down to a nearby well,

> *Don dondaine don!*
> > down to a nearby well,
> *Dondaine, dondaine!*

O very deep the well was, (*bis*)   down to the depth I fell.
By came a horseman riding, (*bis*)   clearly a smart young swell.
"What will you pay for rescue, (*bis*)   rescue from out of the well?"
"Just pull me out," she answered, (*bis*)   "then after that I'll tell."
Once safe on terra firma, (*bis*)   she fled indoors pell-mell.
Close to her window sat she, (*bis*)   singing a gay rondel.
"That wasn't what I asked for. (*bis*)   Kiss me, my lovely belle!
Could you not come to love me, (*bis*)   tell me, my sweet mam'selle?"
"I'll give my heart to someone, (*bis*)   not to a smart young swell.
I'd rather have a soldier (*bis*)   bearded and bold as well."

Only two or three songs in the whole repertory are as well known under various forms, as *The Well Is Deep,* or, as it is sometimes called, *The Water-cress Girl,* from its first line in a variant "J'allais cueillir du cresson." Its long and lively burden, sung by a chorus, alternates with a brief solo, and its alert tune has made this song well suited to work or dance.

That *The Water-cress Girl (La fille au cresson)* enjoyed a considerable popularity in the French provinces admits of little doubt, for a number of records of it are contained in various publications. Champfleury and Wekerlin, for their part, observed that it was a favorite (*fort connue*) among the Dauphiné workmen. This statement is equally true of other areas, principally of the northwestern provinces, where it is likely to have originated. No less than fifty versions of it, compiled from manuscript and printed sources or gathered at first hand in Brittany, were included in Rolland's *Recueil* in the eighties; twenty-five more have since appeared in Millien's Nivernais collection; and from ten to twenty others are to be found in various compilations. If to these we add our Canadian contribution, we find that *At the Well, oh!* possibly excels all other folksongs in the number of records available for comparison.

In a thesis presented in manuscript at the Faculté des Lettres of Université Laval, Quebec, Russell S. Young listed well over 200 versions subdivided into variants, both for old France and New France, about eighty for North America alone. Only *Les Trois beaux canards* may exceed it in numbers for New France.

The well-preserved text, consisting of twelve-syllable lines (6f + 6) and uniform *-on* rhymes, points to a comparatively recent origin, though we would not assume an origin for it later than the seventeenth century, when several of its variants seem to have migrated into Canada with the bulk of the French repertory. Its earliest forms on record are those of Ballard [1] (1711–1724) and of Mme. Favart's comedy *Les ensorcelés . . .* in 1757.[2]

Among the variants of our song we find one in which the maid, less recalcitrant, grants a kiss, two or three if they please, to her gallant rescuers, for fear, it may be, that she might plead in vain another time from the well bottom, or simply because she does not mind paying the penalty, provided, as she herself earnestly urges, that the barons give a pledge of discretion.

The present record, slightly altered from its original form, was obtained in 1918 from Ovide Soucy, one of the best singers in Temiscouata, a county of the lower Saint Lawrence. The equivalent of the long refrain, which is merely one of several found,[3] recurs in scattered parts of France and Quebec, east and west.[4]

The melody is modal, in D (Dorian), with passing modulations that give charm to the ensemble. It seems strange that this grave mode, usually coupled with plain chant and tragic ballads, should so often lend itself to lilting Canadian tunes like this, at the service of rustic craftsmen and weavers. The same may be observed of its form, which is that of a single epic lay rhyming in *-on*.

---

[1] Ballard, *Brunettes et petits airs tendres*, 1711 (in the 1726 edition, cf. tome 3, 296, 297) and *Rondes* (1724)—"Margoton va à l'iau."

[2] Quoted by Rolland: "Mergonton vè et l'iau" in the comedy, *Les ensorcelés, ou Jeannot et Jeannette, par Mme. Favart et Messieurs Guérin et H . . . , représentée pour la première fois par les comédiens italiens du Roi, ler sept. 1757.*

[3] Another refrain also in vogue in Canada is: "O gai, vive le roi. . . . Vive le roi, la reine! . . . Vive Napoléon!" (LaRue, *Le Foyer canadien* 1:355, 356; and *Recueil de chansons canadiennes et françaises,* anon., p. 20).

[4] Two refrains in Millien's collection closely resemble ours: version *e*, "zon, oh j'ai du zi r'zon . . . ," and version *n*, "V'là ti pas de la glinglin glon. . . ."

# REFERENCES AND SOURCES

**Published**

1. F. A. H. LaRue, "Les Chansons populaires et historiques du Canada," *Le Foyer canadien* 1:335, 336: "Vive le roi, vive la reine . . ." (Bibliog. 1).

2–4. Ernest Gagnon, *Chansons populaires du Canada*, "La Bibournoise," 74, 75; "Dondaine don," 70–73; "Gai, vive le roi!" 76–77 (Bibliog. 2).

5. William Parker Greenough, *Canadian Folk-Life and Folk-Lore*, 145, 146: "Gai, vive le roi!" (Bibliog. 4) .

6. Julien Tiersot, *Songs of the People*, "La glin glan glon" (Bibliog. 7).

7. E. Z. Massicotte, in *Le Canard*, No. 19, April 1897, p. 3 (Montreal).

8. Barbeau and Sapir, *Folk Songs of French Canada* 140–142 (Bibliog. 14).

9. Marguerite d'Harcourt, *Chansons populaires du vieux Quebec*, 42, 43 (Bibliog. 45).

10. Barbeau, *Alouette!*, "La fontaine est profonde ziguezon. . . ." (Bibliog. 59).

11. Sœur Marie Ursule, "Civilisation traditionnelle des Lavalois," *Les Archives de Folklore* 5–6:296, 297: "Ma dondaine" (Bibliog. 83).

12. Barbeau, "The Ermatinger Collection of Voyageur Songs," *Journal of American Folklore* 67:141ff. (Bibliog. 92).

**Sources:**

1. Recorded by the author from Mme. Jean Bouchard, Éboulements-en-haut, 1916, No. 95. Version published by Healey Willan in *Chansons canadiennes, ca.* 1929 (Bibliog. 20).

2. The author's version quoted here is from Ovide Souci, Saint-Antonin (Temiscouata), 1918, No. 1908.

3. E. Z. Massicotte, from Marcotte Lapalice, Montreal, 1928.

4. The author, from Felix Mantha, Orléans (near Ottawa), 1941, No. 4206: ". . . Pour pêcher du poisson."

5. François Brassard, in *L'Alma Mater*, Sept. 1941, p. 9: "Quand j'étais chez mon père, Gai, vive le roi!"

6. ——, in *20ᵉ siècle* 4:308, 309 (June, 1946): "Dondaine, don!"

7. ——, from Mme. Alfred Turcotte, Saint-Jérome (Lac Saint-Jean), in 1941: "Roulette, roulons. . . ."

8. J. T. Le Blanc, from Philippe Gaudet, Moncton, N. B., in *La Voix d'Évangéline, ca.* 1950, No. 9982: "Remplir mon cruchon, Bonbon."

9. M. G. Caron, learned from Hilaire Rayon, No. 4690: "Vive le roi, la reine!"

10. The Lacourcière-Savard collection, from Mme. Armand Bouchard, Saint-Siméon (Charlevoix), 1947, No. 279.

11. Luc Lacourcière, from Mlle. Bella Chiasson, Lamèque, N. B., 1950: "La biguenoise. . . ."

12. Frère Onésime Ménard, o.m.i., Ottawa, from Adrien Ménard, Sainte-Justine (Vaudreuil), 1945, No. 4494: "Tu chantes bien Madeleine."

13. Mlle. Pierrette Cousineau, from M. Daignault; collected at the Université de Montréal, 1947: "Rigaudon. . . ."

14–21. The Carmen Roy collection, from L. Collins, La Tourelle (Gaspé), No. 5203b: "Danse bien, Madeleine . . ."; from Pierre Auclair, Rivière-à-Claude (Gaspé), No. 5302: "Dondaine à la wagine . . ."; from Léon Collins, La Tourelle (Gaspé), No. 5556: "Gai, vive le roi . . .", and No. 5584; from Mme. Pierre Landry, Cap-de-Marin (Gaspé), No. 5707: "Dondaine, la migouèné"; from Napoléon Poirier, Saint-Simon (Bonaventure), No. 5717: "Dondaine don!"; from Napoléon Poirier, No. 6533: Chanson de fouleries: "Dondaine don!"; from Benoit Noël, Morris (Gaspé), No. 6778: "Zing! Don! Madelon!"

Add

# IL S'EST MIS À TURLUTTER

## *THERE WAS AN OLD GRANDMOTHER*

C' é--tait u--ne vieill' grand' mè-re, di-gue din dai-ne, qui ne

fai--sait que pleu-rer ——, di-gue din-dé, qui ne

fai--sait que pleurer , qui ne fai---sait que pleurer .

## Il s'est mis à turlutter

C'était une vieill' grand'mère,
>> *Digue dindaine,*
>>>> qui ne faisait que pleurer,
>> *Digue dindé,*
>>>> qui ne faisait que pleurer. (*bis*)
"Qu'a'-vous donc, ma bonn' grand'mère, . . .
>>>> qu'à-vous donc à tant pleurer?"
"Je pleur' ton vieux grand-père . . .
>>>> que les loups ont emmené.
Tous les moutons dans la plaine, . . .
>>>> que les loups ont étranglé."

"Que donneriez-vous, grand'mère, . . .

                si j'allais vous les chercher?"
Il a pris sa turlanline, . . .

                il s'est mis à turlutter.
A vu venir le grand-père, . . .

                ses moutons a ramené.
Ils se sont pris par la patte, . . .

                ils se sont mis à danser.


## There Was an Old Grandmother

There was once an old grandmother,
        *Digue dindaine,*
                who sat weeping hour by hour,
        *Digue dindé,*
                who sat weeping hour by hour. (*bis*)
"Tell me why, my good grandmother, . . .
                you sit weeping hour by hour?"
"I lament your old grandfather, . . .
                whom the wolves by now devour.
And the sheep from our green meadow . . .
                that the wicked wolves have slain."
"What will you give, grandmother, . . .
                if I bring them back again?"
So he took his pipe and tootled . . .
                till the missing flock was found.
And the sheep and old grandfather . . .
                came to her safe and sound.
Then they took them by their trotters, . . .
                and danced a merry round.


This is the westernmost of all the songs in this book, for it was being sung by canoemen as far as the Columbia River in the 1820s,[1] and has been recorded in the last decades at Sainte-Genevieve and at

---

[1] It is one of the eleven songs contained in the Ermatinger collection. See Bibliog. 92.

old Vincennes (southern Indiana). It is also familiar in Canada and Acadia. It was published by Philippe-Aubert de Gaspé in his *Mémoires* (1885) and also by Ernest Gagnon in 1865. Its French source was first made known by Wekerlin, in his *Chansons populaires des provinces de France,* as from Nivernais. But the New World variants, rather than those of the motherland, have preserved a quality of text and tune which derives from its age and poetic tone.[2]

Its lines consist of 7f + 7, with epic cæsura and -é desinence uniformly which makes of it an epic lay. Its tune is in a pipelike modality.

## REFERENCES AND SOURCES

### Published

1. Ernest Gagnon, *Chansons populaires du Canada* 50–53 (Bibliog. 2).

2. Philippe-Aubert de Gaspé, *Mémoires,* 179: "Quand j'étais petite Jeannette . . ." (Bibliog. 3).

3. Julien Tiersot, *Songs of the People,* 62, 63 (Bibliog. 7).

4. Ward Allison Dorrance, "The Survival of French in the Old District of Sainte-Genevieve." 120–129 (Bibliog. 42).

5. Cecilia Ray Berry, *Folk Songs of Old Vincennes,* 34, 35 (Bibliog. 64).

6. Marius Barbeau, "The Ermatinger Collection," *Journal of American Folklore* 67:147ff. (Bibliog. 92).

### Sources:

1. Recorded by: E. Z. Massicotte, from Eugénie (Audet) Malchelosse, Laprairie, 1917.

2. Marius Barbeau, from François Saint-Laurent, La Tourelle (Gaspé), in 1918, No. 2350; reproduced here.

3, 4. J. T. Le Blanc, from "La petite Thérèse," in *La Voix d'Évangéline,* Moncton, N. B.: "Pour endormir les enfants"; and from Mme. Liboire Vautour, Moncton.

5. Marcel Rioux, from Joseph Fraser, Île-Verte (Rivière-du-Loup), 1948, No. 4694.

6. The Carmen Roy collection, from Mme. Zéphirin Dorion, Port-Daniel, 1950.

---

[2] Cf. Ernest Gagnon, *Chansons populaires du Canada,* 50, 52.

# LE DEUIL DU PETIT SAUVAGE
## *THE LITTLE INDIAN'S FUNERAL*

## Le Deuil du petit sauvage

C'était un petit sauvage   tout noir, tout barbouillé,
>    *Ouichté!*
>   *Tourmanangat alahatta watta ouichta,*
>   *Manangat alahatta ouichta, ha! ah!*
S'en fut à la rivière,   c'était pour s'y baigner.
La rivière est profonde,   le sauvage s'est noyé.
Qu'est-ce qu'en port'ra le deuil?   Ce s'ra monsieur l'curé,
Avec sa grand rob' noire   et son bonnet carré,
Aux quatr' coins de sa fosse,   quatr' bouteilles de brandé.

186

# The Little Indian's Funeral

There was a little Indian, dark and dirty he,
>  *Ouitché!*
> *Tourmanangat alahatta watta ouichta,*
> *Manangat alahatta wichta, ha!*

Came strolling by the river bank to bathe one day.
But there! the little Indian was drowned, alas!
They sent for Monsieur le curé to bury him.
In cornered cap and robe of black, the curé came.
He found four brandy bottles—by the bed they lay!

This paddling and work song is a hybrid, with its *petit sauvage* at the opening and its mock Indian burden *Ouichté!*. . . . An improvisation of a *coureur-de-bois* song, it must have brought a smile to the parched lips of day-long paddlers in birchbark canoes, especially with its last words. At each of the four corners of the Indian's grave, "a bottle of brandy lay."

As Ernest Gagnon has observed in his *Chansons populaires*, it was no doubt patterned after the well-known *Malbrough s'en vat en guerre*, in a Quebec variant: "Mon mari est en guerre,/Ne sait s'il reviendra, *Ouichka!* . . ."

Its tune is modern, yet its twelve-syllable lines are epiclike, with epic cæsura at the sixth, and uniform rhymes in *-é*, like an epic lay.

As may be seen below, it has been recorded both in Canada and Acadia, but not in Louisiana.

## REFERENCES AND SOURCES

**Published:**

1. Ernest Gagnon, *Chansons populaires du Canada,* 123 (Bibliog. 2).
2. Barbeau, *Veillées du bon vieux temps,* 24 (Bibliog. 9).

**Sources:**

1. The author's collection, from François Saint-Laurent, La Tourelle (Gaspé), 1918, No. 2364.
2. The J. T. Le Blanc collection, from Mme. Joseph Bordage, Saint-Luc, N. B., in *La Voix d'Évangéline,* Moncton, *ca.* 1938, No. 9263.
3. Recorded by the author and Mrs. Laura Boulton in 1941, from J. B. Dupuis, La Tourelle (Gaspé).

4. Recorded by Marcel Rioux, from Amédée Fraser, Île-Verte, Rivière-du-Loup), 1948.

5. The Carmen Roy collection, from Léon Collins, La Tourelle (Gaspé), in 1951, No. 6635.

6. Recorded by Mlle. Claire Landry, from Marie-Paule Mercier-Lanctôt, Quebec, 1955.

# ALOUETTE!

## AH! THE LARK

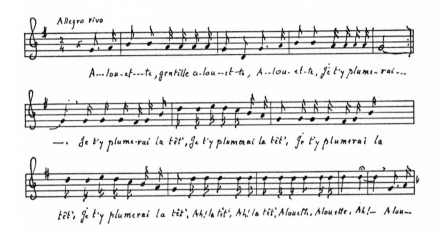

Allegro vivo

A...lou-et----te, gentille a-lou--et-te, A--lou- et-te, Je t'y plume- rai...

—. Je t'y plume-rai la tết', Je t'y plumerai la tết', Je t'y plumerai la

tết', Je t'y plumerai la tết', Ah! la tết', Ah! la tết', Alouette, Alouette, Ah!— A lou—

## Alouette!

Alouette, gentille alouette,
Alouette, je t'y plumerai. (*bis*)
Je t'y plumerai la têt', (*4 fois*)
Ah! la têt', (*bis*)
Alouette, (*bis*)
Ah!

Alouette, gentille alouette,
Alouette, je t'y plumerai. (*bis*)
Je t'y plumerai le bec, (*4 fois*)
Et le bec, (*bis*)
Et la têt' (*bis*) . . .

189

... Je t'y plumerai les yeux ...
    Et les yeux,
    Et le bec,
    Et la têt' ...

*Etc.:* le cou, les ailes, le dos,
      les pattes, la queue ...


## *Ah! the Lark*

Ah! the lark,   gentille alouette!
Ah! the lark,   I'll pluck your feathers! *(bis)*
  I'll pluck feathers off your head. *(4 times)*
    Ah! the head, *(bis)*
    Ah! the lark, *(bis)*
     Ah!

Ah! the lark,   gentille alouette!
Alouette,   I'll pluck your feathers! *(bis)*
  I'll pluck feathers off your bill. *(4 times)*
    Ah! the bill ...

*Etc.:* the neck, the wings, the back, the legs, the tail ...


Originally from France, this enumerative song has, in the past fifty years, grown into the most popular of the Canadian repertory. Its lilt and swing have made of it the conclusion of all the feasts and banquets which come to an end with *Au revoir!*—until we meet again! It has won the favor of countless visitors in French Canada who have easily learned it and repeated it on their way back home. An Australian baseball club, after touring the United States and Canada, was still enjoying it full-throated, forty years ago, on the Vancouver wharf at the edge of the Pacific. Yet not one of the team's members knew a word of French, except those of *Alouette!*

This rigmarole was not so popular formerly as it is today. In our records, we find it only twice, once from the south shore in Gaspé, and once from the north, in the Saguenay. It is mostly on the upper Saint Lawrence that it is well at home.

The folklorist E. Z. Massicotte had this to say in 1917 about the first version he collected for the National Museum: "Few folk songs are as well known to-day as *Alouette*. I find it, for the first time, in my old notebook of 1883. I had learned it in Montreal, where I have lived since childhood. Still it has since achieved world-wide popularity." Ludger Gravel, a Montrealer, has contributed to its repute when, in 1876, he sang it at a banquet of manufacturers in London, England.

A variant of the song was recorded in 1917 by Massicotte at Batiscan, between Quebec and Montreal, from an old man named Ephrem Dessureau, born in 1842. Its words are: "Belle alouette (*bis*), Nous la plumerons. Nous 'i plumerons la tête, Ah! oui, la tête! Brouchte . . ."

A version, collected in 1945 from Jean Lindsay of Roberval, Lake Saint John (Phono. 4460), begins with: "Ah! nous 'i plumerons l'alouette. Nous 'i plumerons tout du long. Ah! nous 'i plumerons la queue (*bis*) . . .

A Gaspé version from François Saint-Laurent, collected in 1918 (Phono. 2370), is somewhat different in its words and tune: "Ah! l'alouette, Qu'elle est gentillette! Ah! l'alouette, Nous t'y plumerons. Nous t'y plumerons la tête." This solo incepit is repeated as loudly as possible by the full chorus. The solo resumes: "Ah! la belle tête. Nous t'y plumerons la tête." (*bis*) "Ah! la tête, la joli' tête!" "Ah! le bec, le beau bec" (*bis*) "Ah! la langue, la joli' langue!" "Ah! l'alouette, Qu'elle est gentillette!" "Ah! l'alouette, nous t'y plumerons . . ."

Quite different is the record (Phono. 2370), also obtained by Massicotte in 1926 from J.-A. Lavallée of Berthier-en-haut: "Nous 'i plumerons la tête de l'alouette (*bis*) Ah! la tête. Dondaine don! Nous 'i plumerons l'alouette, L'alouette, Dondaine don. Nous 'i plumerons l'alouette, Tout du long, Le cou de l'alouette (*bis*). . . ."

In C major, this playful rigmarole does not take the trouble to don a metric form. At best one can say that its refrain contains three accented syllables ending at the cæsura with a feminine ending, and, in the second hemistich, five syllables also closing with a feminine or mute; whereas in the cumulative lines, seven syllables everywhere predominate.

# BIBLIOGRAPHY OF FRENCH-CANADIAN FOLKSONGS

1. LaRue, F. A. H.: "Les chansons populaires et historiques du Canada," *Le Foyer canadien* 1:321–384 (1863)
   Presents about seven songs and explanations.

2. Gagnon, Ernest: *Chansons populaires du Canada,* 1st ed. Librairie Beauchemin, Montreal, 1865
   The first edition, followed by many others, contains about 100 songs with tunes and commentaries.

3. de Gaspé, Philippe-Aubert: *Mémoires,* Quebec, 1885
   Contains the text of a number of folksongs.

4. Greenough, William Parker: *Canadian Folk-Life and Folk-Lore,* George H. Richmond, New York, 1897 (See "Chansons canadiennes," 129–146)

5. McLennan, William: *French Songs of Old Canada,* William Heinemann, Ltd., London, 1904

6. *Chansons canadiennes.* Words and music, harmonized by P. E. Prévost; illustrated by J. C. Franchère. Montreal, 1907

7. *Songs of the People: Forty-four French Folk-Songs and Variants from Canada, Normandy, and Brittany.* Collected and harmonized by Julien Tiersot. G. Schirmer, Inc., New York, 1910.

8. *Chansons of Old French Canada.* Harmonized by Margaret Gascoigne; illustrated by Ethel Seath; introduction by Marius Barbeau. Château Frontenac, Quebec
   Eleven songs drawn from the Gagnon repertoire: both English and French editions.

9. Barbeau, Marius, (ed.): *Veillées du bon vieux temps,* G. Ducharme, Montreal, 1920

10. ——— and E. Z. Massicotte: "Chants populaires du Canada," *Journal of American Folklore* 32:1–89 (1919)
    Introduction and melodies: 46 songs.

11. *Recueil de chants populaires du Canada.* Harmonized by Alfred Laliberté. Max Eschig et Cie, Paris
    Twelve French-Canadian songs presumably drawn from the Gagnon collection.

12. Wyman, Loraine: "Songs from Percé," *Journal of American Folklore* 33:321–335 (1920)
    Fifteen songs with melodies.

13. Lanctôt, Gustave: "Chansons et rondes de Laprairie," *Journal of American Folklore* 33:336–345 (1920)
    Eleven texts and melodies; melodies collected by Marius Barbeau.

14. Barbeau, Marius, and Edward Sapir: *Folk Songs of French Canada,* Yale University Press, New Haven, 1925
    Forty-one songs with introductions, melodies, French and English translations.

15. Barbeau, Marius: "Folk Songs of French Canada," *Empire Club of Canada. Addresses delivered to the members during the year 1925,* Macoomb Press, Toronto, 1925, 180–196

16. ———: *Twelve French Canadian Folk Songs.* English words by Sir Harold Boulton and harmonizations by Arthur Somerwell. Boosey and Co., London and New York, 1927

17. Gibbon, J. Murray: *Canadian Folksongs, Old and New,* J. M. Dent & Sons, Toronto and London
    French and English texts with melodies; mostly drawn from the Gagnon collection.

18. Schaefer, G. A. Grant: *French Canadian Songs,* Arthur P. Schmidt Company, Boston and New York
    Seven songs with words in English and French, presumably drawn from the Gagnon collection.

19. *Vingt-et-une chansons canadiennes—Twenty-one Folk-Songs of French Canada.* Arranged by Achille Fortier, Alfred Laliberté, Oscar O'Brien, Leo Smith, and Ernest MacMillan. Frederick Harris Co., Oakville, Ont., and London, England
    Eight of these songs are from the Gagnon collection; thirteen were collected by Marius Barbeau and E. Z. Massicotte.

20. *Chansons canadiennes—French Canadian Folk-Songs,* 2 vols. Arranged by Healey Willan; collected by Marius Barbeau; translated by Paul England. Frederick Harris Co., Oakville, Ont., and London, England, 1929

21. *Canadian Folk-Song and Handicraft Festival.* Annotated general program, Château Frontenac, Quebec, 1927
    Contains a number of song texts in French and English.

22. *Canadian Folk-Song and Handicraft Festival*. General and daily programs. Château Frontenac, Quebec, 1928

23. Barbeau, Marius: "Folk Songs of French Canada," *Empire Club of Canada. Adresses delivered to the members during the year 1929,* T. H. Best Printing Co., Ltd., Toronto, 1929

24. *Canadian Folk-Song and Handicraft Festival*. General and daily programs. Château Frontenac, Quebec, 1930

25. *Songs of Old Canada: A concert program*. Introduction by Marius Barbeau and Graham Spry, Association of Canadian Clubs, 1928

26. Barbeau, Marius: "Canadian Folk Songs as a National Heritage," *The Canadian Nation*, pp. 18–22 (February, 1928)

27. de Montigny, Louvigny: *Le Bouquet de Mélusine,* Louis Carrier et Cie., Les Editions du Mercure, Montreal and New York; 1928 Contains a number of song texts recorded by Marius Barbeau.

28. *L'Ordre de Bon-Temps (The Order of Good Cheer)*. Ballad opera based on French-Canadian folksongs. Libretto by Louvigny de Montigny; English translation by J. Murray Gibbon; music arranged by Healey Willan; folksongs recorded by Marius Barbeau. Frederick Harris Company, Oakville, Ont., and London, England, 1930

29. Barbeau, Marius: "French and Indian Motifs in Our Music," *Yearbook of the Arts in Canada, 1928–1929,* The Macmillan Company of Canada, Ltd., Toronto, 1929, 125–132

29a. Bridle, Augustus: "Composers Among Us," *ibid.,* 135–140

30. MacMillan, Ernest: *Two Sketches for String Quartet on French Canadian Folk-Songs*. No. 1, "Notre Seigneur"; No. 2, "A Saint-Malo." Carl Fisher, Inc., New York

31. ———: *Four Canadian Chansons Arranged for Male Voices,* Boston Music Co., Boston

32. *A Cycle of Canadian Folk-Songs*. Arranged by Louis Victor Saar for chorus of mixed voices, or three-part women's chorus. Melodies and words from Gagnon (5 songs); English versions by J. M. Gibbon. Carl Fisher, Inc., New York

33. Whitehead, Alfred E.: *French Canadian Folk-Songs*. Arranged for mixed voices (*a capella*); melodies and words from Gagnon (4 songs); English versions by J. M. Gibbon

34. *Chansons canadiennes*. Arrangées pour chœurs à 3, 4, et 5 voix, par l'Abbé J. G. Turcotte, ptre, Trois-Rivières, Quebec

35. Barbeau, Marius: "Folk-Songs of French Canada," *Music and Letters* 13:168–182 (1932)

36. ———: "Deux de nos plus belles chansons," *Revue trimestrielle canadienne* 18:424–439 (December, 1932)

37. Barbeau, Marius: "How Folk-Songs Travelled," *Music and Letters* 15:306–323 (1934)

38. Gauthier, Conrad: "40 chansons d'autrefois," *Le folklore canadien,* Thérien Frères, Montreal, 1932

39. Barbeau, Marius: "Folk-Songs of French Canada," *Transactions of the Royal Society of Canada,* 1935

40. ———: "Folk-Songs of Old Quebec," *National Museum of Canada Bulletin* 75 (Anthropological Series # 16.) 1935

41. ———: *Six Bergerettes from Lower Canada.* Arranged with accompaniment by Ernest MacMillan. Oxford University Press, London, 1935

42. Dorrance, Ward Allison: "The Survival of French in the Old District of Sainte-Genevieve," *University of Missouri Studies* 10, No. 2:120–129 (1935)

43. Barbeau, Marius: "Chansons populaires du vieux Quebec," *Musée national du Canada Bulletin* 75 (Série anthropologique, No. 16.) 1936

44. ———: *Romancero du Canada.* The MacMillan Company, Toronto, and Librairie Beauchemin, Montreal, 1937

45. *Chansons populaires du vieux Québec.* Recueillies et notées par Marius Barbeau; harmonisées par M. Béclard d'Harcourt. Editions de Pierre Schneider, Paris, 1938

46. Barbeau, Marius: "Songs of the Old World," *The Times,* London, May 15, 1939

47. Whitfield, Irène Thérèse: *Louisiana French Folk Songs,* Louisiana State University Press, Baton Rouge, 1939

48. Barbeau, Marius: *Le Soldat canadien chante,* British Empire Service League, Ottawa, 1940

49. ———: *Aux armes, Canadiens!* Hutte canadienne des Chevaliers de Colomb, Ottawa, 1941

50. Anselme, Père, et Frère Daniel: *Chansons d'Acadie,* 1ère série, Montreal, 1942

51. Barbeau Marius: "Voyageur Songs," *The Beaver,* June, 1942, pp. 15–19

52. ———: "Folk-Songs of French Canada," *Educational Record of the Province of Quebec* 59:47–53 (March, 1943)

53. ———: "French-Canadian Folk-Songs," *The Musical Quarterly* 29:122–137 (1943)

54. ———: *Les enfants disent,* Editions Paysana, Montreal, 1943

55. ———: "Modalité dans nos mélodies populaires," *Memoirs Royal Society of Canada* (1944)

196

56. Barbeau, Marius: "Nos belles chansons populaires," *L'Enseignement secondaire au Canada* 23, No. 7: 506–510 (April, 1944)

57. Anselme, Père, et Frère Daniel: *Chansons d'Acadie,* 2ème série, Montreal, 1945

58. Gaudet, Laura C.: *Songs of Acadia (Chants d'Acadie),* Broadcast Music, Inc., New York, 1945

59. Barbeau, Marius: *Alouette! Nouveau recueil de chansons populaires, avec melodies, choisies dans le répertoire du Musée National du Canada,* Éditions Lumen, Montreal, 1946 (Collection Humanitas)

60. Bélanger, Jeannine, et Marius Barbeau: "La césure épique dans nos chansons populaires," *Les Archives de Folklore* 1:131–148 (1946)

61. Barbeau, Marius: "La guignolée au Canada," *French Folklore Bulletin* No. 25:115 (April, 1946)

62. Brassard, François: "Refrains canadiens de chansons de France," *Les Archives de Folklore* 1 (1946)

63. Lacourcière, Luc: "Les Ecoliers de Pontoise . . . ," *Les Archives de Folklore!* (1946)

64. Berry, Cecilia Ray: *Folk Songs of Old Vincennes.* Collected by A. C. O'Flynn and J. M. Carrière. Chicago, 1946

65. Barbeau, Marius: "Canadian Folk-Songs," *University of Toronto Quarterly* (January, 1947)

66. ———: "Come A Singing! Canadian Folk-Songs," *National Museum of Canada Bulletin* 107 (Anthropological Series No. 26.) 1947

67. Brassard, François: "Recordeurs de chansons," *Les Archives de Folklore* 2 (1947)

68. Barbeau, Marius: "Trois beaux canards (92 versions canadiennes)," *Les Archives de Folklore* 2 (1947)

69. Anselme, Père, et Frère Daniel: *Chansons d'Acadie,* 3ème série, Montreal, 1948

70. Barbeau, Marius: "The Blind Singer," *Dalhousie Review* 28 (April, 1948)

71. ———: "Les canciones populares del viejo Quebec," *Folklore de las Americas,* Primiera Antologia, Buenos Aires, 1949

72. Lacourcière, Luc: "Chansons de travestis," *Les Archives de Folklore* 4 (1949)

73. Saucier, Corinne Lelia: "Histoire et traditions de la paroisse des Avoyelles en Louisiane." Thesis at the Faculté des Lettres, Université Laval, Quebec, 1949
    Contains a number of Louisiana folksongs.

197

74. Lemieux, Père Germain, s.j.: *Folklore Franco-Ontarien,* Chansons, Documents historiques, No. 17 (1949)

75. Lacourcière, Luc: "Il est pourtant temps . . . ," *Les Archives de Folklore* 4 (1949)

76. d'Harcourt, Marguerite Béclard: "Analyse des versions musicales canadiennes des 'Trois beaux canards,'" *Les Archives de Folklore* 4 (1949)

77. Barbeau, Marius: "Nos Traditions à l'Université," *Journal of American Folklore* 67:199–211 (1954). For *La blanche biche,* see p. 205.

78. ———: "I Dressed Me All in Feathers," *Journal of American Folklore* 63:181–184 (1950)

79. Brassard, François: "Le Retour du Soldat et le Retour du Voyageur," *Journal of American Folklore* 63:147–157 (1950)

80. Barbeau, Marius: "Folk Songs of Old Quebec," *The Book of Knowledge: Annual,* Grolier Society, Inc., New York, 1951

81. Doyon, Madeleine: "Folk Dances in Beauce County," *Journal of American Folklore* 67:137–146 (1954)

82. Barbeau, Marius: "The Folk Dances of Canada," *Journal of the International Folk Music Council* 3:29 (1951)

83. Ursule, Sœur Marie: "Civilisation traditionnelle des Lavalois," *Les Archives de Folklore* 5–6 (1951)

84. Barbeau, Marius: "Canada," in Thomas and Pikelis, *International Directory of Anthropological Institutions.* Wenner-Gren Foundation for Anthropological Research, 1953

85. ———: "French folklore," in Maria Leach (ed.), *Dictionary of Folklore, Mythology, and Legend,* Funk & Wagnalls Company, New York, 1949, 416–424

86. ———: "Voyageur Songs of the Missouri," *Bulletin Missouri Historical Society* (April, 1954)

87. ———: "La chanson populaire française en Amérique du Nord," *Journal of the International Folk Music Council* 6 (1954)

88. ———: "How the Folk Songs of French Canada Were Discovered," *Canadian Geographical Magazine* (August, 1954)

89. ———: "Canadian (Folk Music)," in Grove's *Dictionary of Music and Musicians,* 5th ed., vol. 3. London, 1954

90. ———: "Canadian Folk Songs . . . ," *Columbia World Library of Folk and Primitive Music,* vol. 8. Compiled and edited by Alan Lomax. New York, 1954

91. ———: "Folk-Song," in Sir Ernest MacMillan, *Music in Canada,* University of Toronto Press, Toronto, 1955

92. Barbeau, Marius: "The Ermatinger Collection of Voyageur Songs (ca. 1830)," *Journal of American Folklore* 67:147–161 (1954)
93. ——: "La complainte de Cadieux, *Coureur de Bois* (ca. 1709)," *ibid.*, 163–183
94. ——: "Nos Traditions à l'Université," *ibid.*, 199–211
95. Fowke, Edith Fulton, and Richard Johnston: *Folk Songs of Canada*, Waterloo Music Company, Ltd., Waterloo, Ont., 1954
96. Stack, Peggy, and Elizabeth Harding: *French Songs for Children*, Novello and Company, London, 1955
    At least two of the songs are from Marius Barbeau's collection for French Canada: "Le Marteau de l'ouvrier," and "Où vas-tu, mon petit garçon?"

*Folksong books, printed or in manuscript:*

97. Laverdière, l'Abbé: *Chansonnier des Collèges,* 1st and 2nd ed., Quebec, *ca.* 1860
    Contains several Canadian folksongs.
98. *Chansonnier manuscript (ca.* 1860). At the Archives du Séminaire de Québec.
    Notebook 10, bearing the names of Abbés Hamel and Doherty, contains a number of Canadian folksongs.

*Folksongs in manuscript theses at the Archives de Folklore, Université Laval, Quebec, and at Université de Montreal:*

99. Mathewson, Dorothy R.: *"French-Canadian Folk-Songs."* Study made for an M. A. thesis, University of Montreal, 1924
100. Adam, Gaston Eugène: "Chansons françaises en Louisiane." A thesis submitted to the Graduate Faculty of Louisiana State University. . . . Department of Romance Languages. Laval University, 1944; August, 1950
101. Brandon, Elizabeth: "Mœurs et langage de la Paroisse de Vermilion en Louisiane." Thesis presented at the School of Graduates, Université Laval, Quebec, with annexed documents, containing many folksongs, 1955

*Recent Publications:*

102. Roy, Carmen: *Littérature orale en Gaspésie,* Musée National du Canada, 1955
     Contains a series of folksongs with the tunes.
103. d'Harcourt, Marguerite et Raoul: *Chansons folkloriques françaises au Canada: Leur langue musicale,* Paris and Quebec, 1956

104. Young, Russell Scott: "Vieilles chansons de Nouvelle France," *Les Archives de Folklore* 7 (1956)

105. Barbeau, Marius: "Folk Songs of French Louisiana," *Canadian Music Journal* 1:10–16 (Winter, 1957)

106. ———: *My Life in Recording Canadian-Indian Folklore,* FG 3502, Folkways Records and Service Corporation, New York, 1957
It contains some French-Canadian folksongs.

# BIBLIOGRAPHY OF FRENCH FOLKSONGS QUOTED HERE

1. Bladé, Jean François: *Dissertation sur les chants héroïques des Basques*, Paris, 1866. *Poésies populaires en langue française recueillies dans l'Armagnac et l'Agenais*, 1879. *Poésies populaires de la Gascogne*, 3 vols. 1881–1882
2. Smith, Victor: "La bergère muette," in "Chansons populaires du Velay et du Forez," *Romania*, No. 13, 110–112
3. Millien, Achille: "Chants et chansons recueillis et classés par Achille Millien; airs notés par J. P. Pénavaire," *Litt. orale et traditions du Nivernais*, 3 vols., avec mélodies, Paris, 1906
4. Arbaud, Damase: *Chants populaires de la Provence, recueillis et annotés par Damase Arbaud*. 2 vols., 1862, 1864
5. Rolland, Eugène: *Recueil de chansons populaires*, 6 vols., 1883–1890
6. Decombe, Lucien: *Chansons populaires recueillies dans le département d'Ille-et-Vilaine*, 1884
7. Doncieux, George: *Le Romancéro populaire de la France*, Paris, 1904
8. Rossat, A.: "Vieilles chansons de France, recueillies dans le Jura bernois," *Shweih. Archi. f. Volks.*, 1910; *La chanson populaire dans la Suisse romande*, Schweis. Gesells, 1917
9. Loquin, A.: "Bibliographie de certains recueils de chants populaires français du 16e et 17e siècle. Livres rares," *Mélusine* 6:217–219 (Cf. *Mélusine* 4: 49–57) (*Mélusine*, 1877, 1884–1900)
10. Beauquier, C.: *Chansons populaires recueillies en Franche-Comté*, 1894
11. Nigra, C.: *Canti popolari del Piemonte*, 1888
12. Luzel, F. M.: *Gwerziou Breiz-Izel*, 2 vols., 1867, 1874
13. Piguet, Edgar: "L'évolution de la Pastourelle au XIIIe siècle à nos jours," *Publication de la Société suisse des traditions populaires*, 148

14. Bujeaud, J.: *Chants et chansons populaires des provinces de l'ouest,* 2 vols., 1865–1866

15. Champfleury and Wekerlin: *Chansons populaires des provinces de France,* 1860

16. Tiersot, Julien: *Chansons populaires des Alpes françaises,* Savoie et Dauphiné, 1903

17. Crane, Thomas Frederick: *Chansons populaires de la France: A Selection from French Popular Ballads.* Edited with introduction and notes.

18. Servettaz, C.: *Chants et chansons de la Savoie,* Paris, 1910

19. Canziani, Estella: *Costumes, Traditions, and Songs of Savoy,* London, 1911

20. de Puymaigre, T.: "Chants populaires recueillis dans la vallée d'Ossau," *Romania* 3 (1874); "Chants populaires recueillis dans le pays messin," 1865

21. de Beaurepaire, Froment: "Chansons populaires du Quercy," *La Tradition* 5–8 (1891–1895)

22. Guillon, C.: *Chansons populaires de l'Ain, recueillies par Charles Guillon.* Préface de Gabriel Vicaire, 1883

23. Orain, A.: "Chansons populaires recueillies dans le département d'Ille-et-Vilaine," *Annales de Bretagne* 16 (1900); *Chansons de la Haute-Bretagne,* Paris, 1902

24. Huré, Jean: *Chansons et danses bretonnes,* Angers, 1902; *Sept chansons de Bretagne,* Paris, 1910.

25. Lambert, Louis: *Chants et chansons populaires du Languedoc,* 2 vols., Paris, 1906

26. Arnaudin, Félix: *Chants populaires de la Grande Lande et des régions voisines,* Paris, 1912

27. Fouquet, A.: *Légendes, contes et chansons populaires du Morbihan,* Vannes, 1857

28. Ballard: *La clef des chansonniers,* 1717; *Mille et un airs,* 1712